Call
& Other
Bantam Ducks

by Scribblers Publishing

Authors; Anne Terrell, Ian Kay and Chris Ashton

Published by Scribblers Publishing Limited

© Scribblers Publishing Limited, 1998. The Watermill, Southwell Road, Kirklington, Notts. NG22 8NQ ENGLAND. Telephone: 01636 816222. Fax 01636 816111

First published in 1998

Printed by Trio Graphics, Gloucester, GL2 5EL. England.

ISBN 1-871644-05-4

Contents

Acknowledgements 4
Origin of Bantam Ducks 5

The Call Duck
An Introduction to Call Ducks by Ian Kay 10

Chapter 1   **Keeping Call Ducks by Anne Terrell** 12
     Stockmanship 16
Chapter 2   **Housing & Fencing** 19
     Housing 19
     The Duck Pen 24
     Fencing 28
     Water 31
Chapter 3   **Feeding** 33
Chapter 4   **Breeding Pens** 37
     Nest boxes 43
     Storage of Eggs 48
     The Broody Call 48
     Hatching by Incubator 52
     Rearing 58
     Artificial Rearing from Day 1 60
     Grading for Breeding & Culling 63
Chapter 5   **Colour Breeding** 67
     Crested Calls 74
Chapter 6   **Showing** 77
     Assessing Calls 83
     Selling Stock 86
     Judging of Ducks by Ian Kay 89
     Suggested standards for non standardised colours
     from The British Call Duck Club 102
Chapter 7   **Preventing Disease** 106
     Ailments 107
Chapter 8   **Predators** 112
Chapter 9   **Breed Summary of the Ideal Call** 123
     A Call Duck's Ability to Adapt 124
     The Magical Eclipse 127

The Black East Indian Duck 128
The Appleyard Duck 142
The Crested Duck 158
     Terms Explained 162
     Different Types of Travelling Boxes 164

ACKNOWLEDGEMENTS

I would like to say how much I have enjoyed writing these few pages on one of the loves of my life 'The Call Duck'.
While it was not difficult to find the words, what was difficult was finding the time. I needed to consider before I got the 'new fangled gadget' out (computer to those of you living in the modern world) whether I ought to be doing something else, for once I started the hours slipped away. I have to admit to seeking a little help here and there when I deemed it necessary to consult on a particular facet of this hobby, for there are more ways than mine of keeping Calls. What did surprise me was that I learnt little I didn't already know and had a few surprises discovering the technique of others.

My thanks must go to Tony Penny for giving me many hours of his time, to Stuart Philpott for a very long telephone call, to Mike Griffiths, the bane of my life on the telephone but a staunch supporter, to John Hall who gave of his time at the busiest time of the year and to all those whose brains I picked without them ever knowing it.

To the Publishers of this tome my heartfelt thanks must go to Stuart Kay who thought nothing of getting up at 4 a.m. to visit Cornwall or Devon and talk for many hours, leaving to return home at least 13 hours after he had left it. His support made it possible for me to write with confidence. If he doesn't become an expert breeder of Calls it will be through no fault of mine or Tony Penny's! Thanks also to him for sorting out my chatterings and putting them into some sort of order.

I sincerely hope I have done 'the little duck' justice. Good luck to the beginner. Keep trying, I still am after more than 20 years. Remember there is always something left to learn. ANNE TERRELL

We would like to thank Anne, Chris and Ian for the courage and time to put pen to paper and share their experiences and knowledge with us all. Thanks to John Soper, Tony Penny and Graham and Sandra Barnard for supplying us with quality birds to photograph and refreshments during the visits.
We are also indebted to Glynda Green our proof reader, Ulanda Kay for the drawings and Evelyn van Vliet for most of the photography in the book. Evelyn is a keen Call duck breeder who enjoys taking their photographs. Thanks for all the hours taking and even more, the hours selecting the ones for this book. SCRIBBLERS PUBLISHING LIMITED.

The Origin

The origin of Bantam ducks has never been conclusively proved. We therefore reprint several articles on the subject which have been written by respected writers and allow you to reach your own conclusion.

Lewis Wright's Book of Poultry is considered by many to be the 'Bible' in the exhibition poultry world. This book was printed in several publications, each one being updated to events at that period. If we consult the one printed in 1894 Wright states a decline in interest in the Call duck for exhibition purposes. However they were still being used as decoys on the shooting ponds.

Mallard Call ducks illustrated by Lewis Wright in 1894

No attempt is made to establish their origin, even though several paragraphs are devoted to the origin of the Black East Indian Ducks. He describes the breed as being as small as possible having a short bill and a prominent forehead. Only two colours are described, White and Grey (Mallard).

In the book 'Our Poultry' written by Harrison Weir and published a few years later, two pages are allocated to Call ducks. Firstly, Weir describes their use as decoys over the preceding years, with detailed accounts of the catching pens. He then writes that their existence in England is not recorded, but quotes from a book written by Francis Willughby during the seventeenth century where they are described as 'Coy' ducks, which my dictionary translates as meaning playfully demure. He also quotes from Johnson's Dictionary which was written in 1755 the word Kooi meaning cage in the Dutch language.

When describing the breed he states that many of the English Decoy ducks differ little from the wild Mallard, with some of the birds having interbred with the common domestic duck. He then continues to say that with the introduction of a much smaller version, which had been developed in Holland, a different type was emerging. These new birds were known as 'Dutch Call Ducks'. They had apparently been created by interbreeding and probably the introduction of fresh stock which was different in body shape. It has been suggested that many of these Calls were imported into Holland from the Dutch East Indies.

Harrison concludes the chapter by expounding his appreciation of the small Call ducks with their peculiar piping call and inquisitive, yet attractive nature. Again he quotes them as being in White or Grey colouring. He describes the Whites as having full Dutch boat shaped bodies, short beaks and rounded heads with short bills of a deep bright orange tint and standing on a pair of short, and equally brightly coloured shanks and feet. All of which would suggest that the ones which had been successfully shown during the previous half century were the true Dutch Call as opposed to some crossbred Mallards.

A pen and ink drawing by Harrison Weir from 1903 showing White and Grey Call ducks he bred that year.

In several of the books reference is made to Darwin's observations on the Call duck, where he states that when caught from the wild they can easily be domesticated. It is a pity he did not also state where you could go and catch them in their natural wild habitat.

After the death of Lewis Wright in 1905, there was a continuation of a similar type of book entitled 'The Encyclopaedia of Poultry'. Again, this was published in several updated versions. The one which I am referring to was printed during the 1930s. Call ducks in this edition are not classified under Domestic Ducks, but under the Wildfowl, along with Teal, Widgeon, Carolina, etc., which suggests that Stephen Hicks, who was responsible for updating the original print, did not consider them a true showing breed as they are at the present time. Their description is very brief, but again mention is made of Darwin describing them as being remarkably small. Again they are stated as existing in only the White and Grey colouring.

One of the most gifted writers and artists during this period was Cornelis van Gink. He was born in Holland and should therefore be well acquainted with Dutch Call ducks. We reproduce here, in full, an article which he wrote for Feathered World in 1932, I find him very constructive and possibly the most enlightening of all the writers quoted in this chapter.

A beautiful Blue-fawn Call duck. Bred and exhibited by Tony Penny

The Dutch Call Ducks

Although of late years very little attention has been given in Holland to the breeding of the very interesting little Dutch Call Ducks, every now and then we have met some really good stock, and even at smaller shows.

Call Ducks can be kept, owing to their small size, with very little swimming water, and will keep in good condition even in very limited quarters; but, noisy as they are, they have to be kept at a little distance from the house.

The Call Duck of pure strain is really a dwarf or Bantam duck, being much smaller than the wild duck, the latter being about twice the size of a fine Call Duck. There are white and Grey Call Ducks, but the greys have never been bred to the same quality as the white ones.

According to a reliable English illustration about seventy-five years ago, there must have been better Grey Call Ducks than there are today, the birds reproduced being smaller and more compact in shape than the modern type.

About the origin of this breed of ducks there has been much difference of opinion, to a certain extent due to the fact that there have been ordinary shaped Dutch Call Ducks. The Dutch Call Ducks have been described in old English books under the name of 'Dutch Dwarf Ducks' and 'Dutch Call Ducks'.

Whereas the ordinary Call Ducks were only tamed descendants of white, or nearly white, wild ducks, the Dutch were smaller in size and differently shaped.

No definite information is known about the origin of the Dutch Call Ducks, but the marked difference in shape of head and bill leads to the conclusion that they are not dwarfed specimens from the ordinary wild duck of Western Europe. We are led to believe that they are bred from stock imported from the orient in former centuries. The small black East Indian ducks are proof of the fact that there are small-sized ducks in the far orient. We even believe that the ancestors of the present Dutch Call Ducks which reached Holland were white in colour, and ever since the first descriptions of the breed appeared in print the white variety has been considerably better in quality than the grey one.

As old pictures prove, pure Chabo or Japanese Bantams of the black-tailed buff variety were to be found in Holland in the seventeenth century. There is a possibility that importations were made by Dutch captains from Japan, making use of the fact that no other nation, for a long period, could trade with Japan. Then we should not be surprised if some day Japanese poultry and duck fanciers might find in their old books information relating to *some old breed of dwarf ducks, especially as the Call Duck's type is very different to the ordinary European type of duck to sport from it, and since they breed so true they must be a very old-established breed.*

The Dutch Call Ducks must be quite horizontal in build, short and cobby, with a round thick head and a short, nicely rounded bill. The more compact in shape and the rounder in head and shorter in beak the more valuable they are. Their colour should be pure white, but they are usually more or less yellow-tinted.

Although sensitive to damp night quarters, they are quite hardy as long as their coop is dry and well littered with clean straw. The females lay quite well, and, just as in bantams, their eggs are big in proportion to the size of their body. The ducks are reliable sitters, and rear their ducklings very well. In former years Call Ducks were largely used for hatching and rearing rare and small ornamental ducks.

Moving quickly forward to recent times, another respected Dutch writer Hans Schippers wrote an article for the Fancy Fowl monthly publication. His well illustrated observations on Call ducks were printed during 1997 and extracts from them are as follows; The Call duck is known in Holland as the 'Kwaker', where it is claimed to be of Dutch origin, but actually came from the East Indies. The birds themselves have been in Holland for many centuries where they are considered to be a very cute and sociable little duck which give you so much pleasure and satisfaction that once you have kept them you cannot live without them. To most fanciers they have become an addiction!

He continues that nothing is written to confirm their origin, but most probably they were transported to the Netherlands by ships sailing from the Dutch colony in the East Indies. Another theory which again is not substantiated is that Laysan Teal were used to create the well recognised smaller type of Call which is associated with Holland. The Laysan Teal carries many of the characteristics associated with the Call duck, such as a short and compact body, orange legs, the typical concave bill skull line and a shrill quacking, and an active and inquisitive nature.

The Call Duck

An Introduction to Call Ducks by Ian Kay

Call Ducks have been bred in the British Isles for a longer period of time than many people imagine, certainly over 150 years.

They were originally used in the trapping of other breeds of wildfowl. The Calls were tethered into the catching nets and their distinctive call attracted the unsuspecting visitors into the traps, hence their name of Call Duck or Decoy Duck. Other variations of the name have also been used.

Call ducks were shown during the nineteenth century and reference is made to them in many of the books written during this period. The 'Illustrated Book of Poultry' written by Lewis Wright was published in several updated editions. The one printed in 1890 states that the popularity of Calls has declined in recent years due to the introduction of showing Mandarin, Carolina, Teal, etc., the breeds all being classified as 'Ornamental Ducks'.

In recent times their rise to prominence started around 1980. The British Waterfowl Association was discouraging the exhibiting of most Ornamental Waterfowl, even though the birds were still being shown in America and Europe. Consequently they allocated separate classes for Call Ducks. The B.W.A. club show in 1981 was held at the Alexandra Palace in London. A single class for Call Duck, any colour or sex was included in the schedule and attracted 12 entries. These were mostly white coloured and were slightly larger in size than many of today's winning birds.

The next decade was to witness the most rapid rise in popularity and excellence of any breed since the exhibiting of small livestock commenced. It is interesting to note that the breed's decline in popularity and revival 100 years later were in direct relation to the showing of the decorative and very diminutive wild fowl breeds.
In his book, Lewis Wright describes the ideal Call as being 'As small as possible and having a short bill, with a prominent forehead, or, as Pigeon breeders would call it, a 'good stop'. All of this would appear to be applicable a century later. During this period, Calls were only shown as Whites or Grey, i.e. Mallard coloured. The present day Call duck is probably much smaller than its original ancestors. Indeed, there is still a trend to

decrease its size still further with the possible threat to the breed's success. The birds must not be allowed to develop to a point where we are showing 'freaks' rather than birds which can consistently breed to the same conformation and type. Many judges place great emphasis on their ball shaped head and short bill, often at the expense of body shape and carriage which collectively carry a larger number of points in the breeds standard of perfection.

The great interest in Call ducks has allowed the breed to develop into a vast range of attractive colour patterns. Many of these have been originally created in the U.S.A. and their popularity has quickly transferred to Britain.

The popularity of Call and other breeds of miniature duck is still expanding with new enthusiasts annually joining the band of established breeders. The following chapters in this book give expert advice on keeping and breeding all types of domesticated miniature ducks and should prove compulsive reading to both beginners and long standing stalwarts of the breeds.

Mallard Pied Call duck, 26 weeks old, bred and exhibited by John Kay and Son. slightly flat on its crown, but will develop with age.

Chapter 1 - Keeping Call Ducks by Anne Terrell

Having decided that you want to own this most delightful of ducks, the Call, many things should be taken into consideration. Where are you going to obtain them, where are you going to put them, how are you going to keep them, what will you feed them on, what will you put water in, do you want to breed them for pleasure or for showing or just keep them for pets?

Obtaining a pair of Call Ducks is easy until you decide that you want a pair now and then the problems begin. You will have seen numerous adverts with Calls for sale in the local paper and club magazines or seen birds for sale at auctions or markets, then mysteriously, there suddenly appear to be none on offer. There are certain times of the year when they are prolific and certain times of the year when they are all but unobtainable. When you have discovered the breeder nearest to you an order can be placed or you can ring him or her up in June, July or August and see what has been bred that year. To discover who breeds Calls you need to get in touch with the various organisations devoted to waterfowl or go to a local poultry show where there is a section for waterfowl. The Secretary of the show can usually put you in touch, if not with the actual person, with somebody who will know. The time not to be looking for Calls is when the breeding season has started and breeders have sold their surplus stock and are now in the process of creating a new generation. March to June are the months when stock for sale is scarce on the ground but even then it is possible to find some if you try hard enough. However, if you time it right, a visit to the breeder before the selling season starts in earnest is recommended, for then you have the pick of the bunch. Be warned; finding an odd duck poses something of a problem, as in most seasons more drakes are bred than ducks. Sod's Law reigns in that if you are to lose a bird it will be the female. Most breeders, I suspect, hold their breath when asked 'Have you any Call Ducks for sale? I have lost one of mine,' especially after the Christmas break, for it is during the winter that the fox strikes or a weakened bird dies in extreme weather. Should the request be for a female the answer is usually, 'No'. One can be sure that if a female is available the colour is wrong. However, few of us dispose of all our spare drakes, for apart from anything else, we may need them ourselves. My advice here would be to buy a trio of Calls but this is almost always impossible. Should you be lucky, be prepared to pay a fairly high price, for female Calls are at a premium.

If it is pet ducks you require, the breeder probably has some that he can recommend which are not anything very special, but if he is well up in the show world they may well produce the odd special duckling. Many a breeder has an experimental pen which he has put together to give himself birds which will provide an outcross that complements his main stock, and every reputable breeder has those birds which produce just the odd show specimen and are kept for that purpose.

Perhaps you have decided it is birds that will be suitable for showing that you require but which will not win at any of the major shows. These are the birds I recommend. You can get your hand in and learn all there is to know about showing a bird, meet the people who can help you and, having bought birds of sufficient standard, with luck, breed your own show winner, if not next year, the year after.

1. Anne comments 'Character oozes from the Call' and this white female of Tony Penny's shows it. She would not stay still, wanting to come to the camera and see what we were doing and quacking loud and proud.

The breeder will have several birds that come from show winners but which are not quite show winners themselves. It is a fact of life that the stars of the show world do not reproduce prolifically. They do as a rule lay but perhaps not quite so many eggs as their slightly inferior sisters. The eggs from the good birds are also difficult to hatch whilst the eggs from their siblings probably hatch more easily and there are far more of them to experiment with. These are the birds for you.

Maybe you have decided you want to start at the top and buy birds that are of show quality and may perhaps win. One cannot be confident of this until at the show for, every season, one never quite knows what will have been produced until it is seen in the show pen. If you are extremely lucky the breeder may have a pair of excellent show quality birds that he is willing to part with. Be prepared to open your purse wide for he will not sell them cheaply. You are asking to start at the top and must pay for the privilege.

The Call Duck is special to all those who have been fortunate enough to discover this delightful little duck. It is the dwarf of the domestic breeds and the most popular. To own a pair of Call Ducks is to be 'hooked'. Once smitten by 'the lure' of the Calls there is nothing to do but submit to the inevitable and enjoy it. Of all the breeds of domestic waterfowl the Call is the smallest and at the Waterfowl Shows the classes staged are numerous and well supported. Being compact, it is easy to cater for and economical to feed. It can be adequately kept in the minimum of space and its very smallness gives it the advantage that, where the larger heavier birds will poach up the ground in very wet weather, the Call will leave it relatively unscathed. Perhaps its one drawback is the noise the female Call makes but this tends to be worse in the autumn when it definitely lives up to its name and tells us the reason for which it was created. It has to be said the Call female is noisy and if there are several the volume can be quite deafening. Young females seem to shout more than older birds and when one opens its beak to declare its presence there seems to be nothing for it but that the rest must join in. Sympathetic neighbours are needed or neighbours not only with double glazing but a collection of Calls themselves!

Character oozes from the Calls and they are forever up to something. Tales abound of these imps of the domestic waterfowl world and the enjoyment they give is infinite. One is never short of another tale to tell and it is a joy to listen to a doting owner relate the latest escapade his or her birds have enacted. They can be extremely infuriating, stubborn and exasperating but they are never dull. They are fearless when it comes to defending their own and it is rather startling to have a little duck launch itself at you when defending its young. It is not unknown for large ducks to be removed from a pen containing Calls when they have bullied and intimidated the life out of them. A pinch from a Call, which you are ignoring and which is demanding attention, is extremely painful and unexpected to say the least. Visiting dogs have also been known to run for their life pursued by a tiny fiend which will not accept that if the 'worm' turns it will be mincemeat. They are staunchly loyal in their partnerships and one must take care when one decides to split up an established pair. Perhaps it is better not to if the pair is successful in producing good offspring for if the birds are not split at the right time of the year the owner will find himself with a duck that will not shut up and a drake who runs the fence trying to become reunited with her. Infertile eggs will be the order of the day. Once bonded they will stick to their own even if in a pen with another pair or trio. However, forays into the other drakes' territories are undertaken and the odd egg hatches when perhaps it would be politic to question the parentage of the resulting duckling. We will not credit the Call drake with total fidelity but take his favourite duck away and he will let you know!

There is infinite variety when it comes to the number of colours to choose from and these seem to increase yearly so be prepared to put up another enclosure and yet another. Some people prefer to keep to the original established colours while others look for the odd different looking duckling each year and eagerly await the time when it colours up. White and Apricot are probably the most popular but there is something to be said for all of the colours. To breed a Call that is the epitome of the standard and which is the right colour to boot must be everybody's dream but standards are set to breed to and achieving the perfect duck would be a sad disappointment and to breed a whole string of perfect ducks a total disaster. When standards are set they describe the ideal, when or where in life does one find one's ideal? Life is a compromise and so it has to be when breeding any creature. Call ducks are not easy to breed so anybody hoping for instant success must think again. The most perfect pair of birds does not necessarily produce good birds. The also rans you have put to one side, perhaps to use as foster parents or just in case something happens to the main birds, are just as likely to produce that special duckling, especially if they have in their family tree prize winning bothers and sisters.

It would seem that the majority of people take as their first colour white but this is a most difficult colour to start with. The competition is fierce at the shows with extremely large classes and so the chances of success are few unless you have been fortunate enough to find a successful breeder who regularly wins on the show bench and who just happens to have a very good pair to spare. Much better to start with a coloured pair and get your hand in. You will then have some idea of the difficulties pertaining to breeding show standard Calls and gain experience in the field of breeding.

It must be remembered that while this little duck is delightful, audacious, time consuming and infinitely versatile it is also frustrating. No one should assume that having acquired a pair that he or she is going to breed good Call Ducks the next season just like that. You may not manage to breed any at all. It can be considered a major disadvantage to have bred the larger domestic birds before turning to the miniatures, for the management of the Calls is very different. The adult birds are small and, therefore, far more vulnerable. The eggs and ducklings are small and as a consequence must be treated with great care. Call ducklings, especially high standard Call ducklings are fragile little beings and need intensive care. In the ensuing chapters it is hoped to give some idea of the needs of the Calls and the best way to be successful.

Stockmanship

I think for some people stockmanship is inbred in them and they instinctively know what to do when. This does not mean that it cannot be acquired although those of us without it will never quite have the magic of those with it. Stockmanship really consists of hard work, a good eye for detail and making sure when we visit the duck run that before we leave we have checked every last detail. Things run smoothly much of the time but at different times of the year it is necessary to put in an extra effort. The breeding season is an obvious case for extra vigilance and most of us give it without even thinking about it for we are intent on coming out at the end with a new crop of promising youngsters. Weather brings to mind the need for stockmanship with a vengeance. In very hot weather it is necessary to ensure that our birds have sufficient shade in which to shelter from the sun and an adequate supply of clean water that does not run out. To have to endure the heat of the day for many hours without sufficient shade is to ask too much of our birds. To ask them to endure it without a source of water to go to is nothing short of cruelty. While food is important water is vital.

A good Call should be round and deep as shown by this excellent Grey female.

The winter months can also bring hardship and a need for us to exert ourselves. If water is frozen birds are once again deprived. If there is snow on the ground life is bleak. Those birds that are housed can be left in their houses but even here care is needed. Water will have to be put inside and water makes a mess. To ask our birds to endure cold is one thing, to have them endure it in wet filthy conditions is another. Not only are they miserable, damage is done to plumage and disease can break out. Birds that are housed within a perimeter fence can escape when snow drifts up against the wire. Where they can get out the fox can walk in. I have listened to people saying they have lost their birds because a snowdrift had enabled a fox to enter the pen. Why did they not take a shovel and clear the snow away? The answer is simple, application and hard work. When the temperature descends to below freezing and stays there, hardship faces our birds. They can cope given the means to do so. Ponds must be cleared of ice and topped up with fresh water. If this is not possible it is better to leave large expanses of water covered in ice rather than break the coating in a small area. Birds can get carried away when the ice is first opened up and when diving can find themselves trapped under the remaining ice. Much better to place a container of fresh clean water beside the pond. This can be emptied each night and filled early the next morning. An area can be strewn with straw and in strong freezing winds a semi-circle of straw bales will give shelter. Food in the form of pellets should be given ad lib to keep body temperature up and give your birds something to fight the cold with. If after you have done all this you still lose a bird or two it is either very bad luck or the bird is not strong enough to survive. If this is the case it's much better to find out in the winter when there is a chance you may be able to replace it, rather than a death at the start of the breeding season which spoils all your plans for the year.

In early January 1997 we were frozen solid in the piggeries but did manage to keep taps dribbling 24 hours a day after mending the leak one of them had sprung on Boxing Day, 1996. Thirty two buckets of water were carried twice a day to water the pigs in residence at the time and an equal number for the birds. When the ponds froze to the bottom and there was the risk that they might become damaged if we continued to break the ice, washing up bowls were placed where needed and filled as required. These were emptied every night to avoid them becoming frozen solid and filled early the next morning. One year when the piggeries and all the taps froze in the duck runs we were carrying water from the house. That was hard work!

In short Stockmanship is the looking after and caring for your birds. Experience is gained, as a rule, at the expense of the creatures.

Crested bantam ducks bred by Tony Penny.

Chapter 2 - Housing & Fencing

Housing

Whether buying or constructing accommodation for your birds yourself, the first consideration must be size. I would go so far as to say no house is too big but many houses will be too small. Ducks by their nature are messy and the house will need frequent cleaning out if it is to remain hygienic. A house that is 5' x 6' with a good grass run should manage 2 drakes and 4 ducks without overstocking the area. Adequate ventilation is a must to ensure that the air the birds are breathing is clean. It is also paramount that the bedding be kept as dry as possible for various ailments will be encouraged by filthy bedding.

If the house is constructed of wood with a solid floor, adequate ventilation at the top near the roof is necessary to maintain a flow of clean air. The door should fit well and be secure. Whilst ducks do not roost, the height of the house will govern the quality of the air within it. Hot air rises and ducks do not require to be kept warm, having a superb set of feathers and down to do the job for them.

This photograph taken at John and Sylvia Soper's shows their Call pens with protective netting over the top.

It is best to have the roof sloping away from the front where the ventilation is situated so that all rain water is carried to the back of the house. If the house is faced towards a hedge this will limit the amount of rain which is blown into it. If the fence surrounding the enclosure is fixed to the back of the house, the rain which runs off the roof will not be dibbled into a sea of mud by the birds, thus keeping the run as mud free as possible.

Having ascertained where you are to obtain your birds and what colour (it should be noted that some colours are more popular than others and consequently while more are bred they are often difficult to obtain as the demand is high), then you must turn your thoughts to how you are going to house them. There can be no doubt that birds which are kept out all the year within a stockproof fence do better than birds that are shut up each night in a shed. There is a certain amount of stress attached to being chased into a house every night and then let out in the morning. Also, while in the house, the birds cannot see what is happening outside and must at times be rather apprehensive. If they are allowed to live free within the confines of a fence, able to see all around them and to roost on or near water, they have to all intents and purposes the situation under control and can take evasive action if necessary. The fact that a fox might manage to breach their perimeter fence is not for them to worry about but you the owner.

However, it is not always possible to give birds ideal conditions and it is by no means impossible to be highly successful if the birds are shut up.

After this Dutch farmer has milked and fed his cattle he goes down stream in his boat to feed his ducks. Note the breeding and shelter cabin located on the side of the canal.

While a pair of Calls do not take up a great deal of space, the bigger the house the better. A house just big enough for two becomes inadequate when the first breeding season is over. You have been successful and wish to retain more ducks. Also, there is insufficient room to incorporate a nest box or two for the female to lay in. The run attached to the house should also be as big as possible not only for the reason above but also to ensure that the ground does not become a sea of mud during the winter when the grass does not grow and the beaks and feet are working overtime. Small they may be but they still have webbed feet and busy beaks. If the pen does become excessively muddy it is too small and consequently overstocked. Mud around the drinker is to be expected but can be minimised by putting the water container on a raised concrete platform or on a bed of gravel.

A wooden house is probably best as it is self insulating. Building a concrete block or brick construction is permanent and thought must be given as to whether that is really where you want the house to be for all time. Metal is cold in the winter and condensates; during the summer it turns into an oven. A good solid floor to the house ensures that should a fox decide it wants an easy dinner it cannot dig into the house and kill at its leisure because the birds cannot get away. When one decides to keep these creatures then one becomes responsible for their well being and owes it to them to do one's best. How many times have you heard, 'It was the one time I forgot to shut them up,' or 'I never dreamt a fox would do that.' They do frequently. There are times, unfortunately, when one simply cannot win and the loss is great not from a financial point of view, for the sums of money that change hands in the purchase of Call Ducks is not by today's standards great, it is the time lost that is so devastating. Perhaps you have been pursuing a certain breeding programme over several years and you are just beginning to get the results you require and consequently making a name for yourself. You find your stock is sought after and you are winning, not just at the local shows but against real competition at the major shows. To lose your key birds or the results of breeding your key birds can put you back several years and negate all your achievements.

It is inadvisable to house Calls with large birds e.g. Aylesburys. While they may live happily together for a period of time, eventually the Call will suffer. A sudden fright while in the house can result in the Call being trampled on and, while this may not kill it, serious injury can result. With the advent of the breeding season, should the larger drake decide he has not enough mates of his own to satisfy him, the Call female will suffer greatly from his attentions. Conversely it is not unknown for the larger birds to be persecuted by the Call drake who is, at times, pugnacious to say the least.

Greater success can be achieved with adequate space where the birds are not confined over night but a close eye should be kept to ensure that the larger drake is directing his attentions to his own mates. It does not need me to point out what the results will be if he does not.

There are no ends to which the true enthusiast will not go to pursue his hobby. Wanting to keep and breed the 'little duck' and only having a moderate garden need be no obstacle to keeping more than one pen of birds and more than one colour. A garden I am thinking of is fenced down each side and across the bottom (leaving the centre free), divided into several individual pens each with its own house of sufficient size to house four to six Calls for the breeding and selling season, unless too much rain turns them into a mud pit. A large shed is constructed which is big enough to house all the stock birds during the rest of year when it is necessary to rest the breeding pens. Leading off from this house is a concrete standing onto which the birds are allowed during daylight hours. As each pen is rather small and the ducks need to be shut up over night, eggs are picked up every day to be set in an incubator each week.

While the birds are housed with access to the hard standing and consequently have access to limited space a high degree of stockmanship is called for in that the hard standing must be kept clean at all times for the likelihood of disease will be high. The house must be kept at a high standard of cleanliness. Clean water will be most important.

When the stock birds are moved to their breeding quarters the house and concrete can be thoroughly cleaned and await the arrival of the current season's youngsters. The centre of the garden which has been left free is where the young, which are reared in the garage, will be put after they have come off heat to grow up. This area is left unstocked throughout the winter and early spring to rest the ground.

The drawbacks to this method are many but with good planning and a high standard of stockmanship nothing is impossible. One of the biggest problems is the weather, for birds cannot be split up into breeding pens until the drier weather arrives, for to put them out too early will mean the poaching up of the carefully preserved pens. These pens will not recover for the rest of the year. As the birds are all kept within the same area they will have decided for themselves which partner they want for the season and, if this is not your choice, split up into the breeding pens they will call to each other and do their best to become reunited. The inevitable result will be clear eggs when the birds are first put out if the duck has already commenced laying. The drakes will also take a while to settle. In a late wet spring this will mean the shortening of the laying season and consequently fewer eggs laid.

In north Holland some breeders construct small pens on the side of the ditches as nesting and resting areas.

Care must be taken to watch for signs of disease for it will spread like wildfire while the birds are housed in close confinement. Concrete is not the ideal medium for a long stay for it is wearing on the feet but the Call must score in this department for it is light. Should there be worms present these also will spread and a worming programme must be adhered to.

With so many birds in close confinement there will be much to tempt predators. Food in the form of wheat can be fed under water to minimise loss but, inevitably, rats will also be attracted. Call ducks are small and should a pregnant female rat arrive unexpectedly and become entrenched under the house she will find herself with a ready source of protein to sustain her pregnancy and feed her young. It is amazing how rats can creep up on one and become a plague before one knows it. Losses can be high with so many birds kept together in a confined space. Unfortunately, often the first one knows of the presence of a breeding female rat can be when one opens up the shed to discover a number of dead birds. In fact any predator that decides to pay a visit can do significant damage.

Another photo showing the ditch pens in Holland.

Care must be taken also with the ground set aside for the rearing of the year's hatch. In a good season it will become very worn and in a wet season very muddy and fouled. This ground needs to be carefully looked after and rested as much as possible.

A very high degree of stockmanship and dedication is needed to keep birds in the conditions I have described above. A tremendous amount of hard work and vigilance is entailed but it can be and is done.

The Duck Pen

When you have bought or constructed as big a house as you can either afford or accommodate and laid plans for several houses for different colours or offspring retained, a run is needed and here again care must be taken that it does in fact keep the birds in. It is very tempting to give them the run of the entire garden but, again, how safe will they be?

What one requires is the maximum number of viable eggs with the minimum amount of fuss. Birds that are shut up every night and have their eggs continually taken away are likely to give up. Why should they continue to lay when all their efforts are being frustrated. They drop eggs willy nilly, hang on to their eggs until they are let out and steal a nest in the garden or run to have these secreted eggs discovered and taken. Within the confines of a fox proofed fence with an adequate supply of nest boxes they can lay a clutch and begin the process of incubation themselves thus giving a much better chance to the successful incubation of these eggs.

If the entire garden is securely fenced then by all means give the birds the run of it but do remember the bottom of the gate. It has been known for me to leap out of the kitchen window into the neighbour's to cut a duck off which was heading blithely for the water meadows down the road. Once there I should have been hard pushed to re-capture it.

Inside Graham and Sandra's enclosure is a pond which is segregated into 3 different pens, all birds having access to the water. These will become their breeding pens each holding a trio of Calls.

They are excellent gardeners in that they eat the pests that can decimate young plants but do themselves find things like young lettuces very much to their taste. It is most beneficial to the ducks to range the garden picking up the various bugs as it gives them an extra source of completely natural protein making the yokes of the eggs darker in colour and more viable when it comes to hatching. The more you put in the more you get out is a very good maxim to operate by. I had a customer who ran a market garden growing pinks, rhubarb and strawberries, and I used to obtain for him female Runners and Khaki Campbells. These were allowed to free range the property and were very efficient at ferreting out the slugs and snails which ate the ripening strawberries. They were also allowed through the glass houses growing the pinks and through the tunnels bringing on the early strawberries. Having been watched through binoculars they were seen not to eat the strawberries as did a pair of geese. They laid loads of beautiful eggs which were sold at the door. One way or another they earned their keep. However, a diet of special waterfowl breeders' pellets or layers' pellets and a substantial run will do just as well as free range and the birds will be safe. A fence will keep the birds safe from chance encounters with danger. While one's own cat does not as a general rule kill one's own birds the neighbour's cat does not play by the rules and can cause havoc or indeed so can a visiting friend's dog. Owning one's own cat will help to keep visiting cats away for cats are territorial. Entire females will, I fear, entice entire toms at certain times and the courting over your birds may provide a tasty treat.

A simple but effective cabin built by John Soper to provide breeding pens for his ducks with access to the ponds.

If you should buy stock that are full winged it is tempting to leave them in this condition and it cannot be denied that to see one's birds circling the property in full flight is a marvellous sight. People do keep them full winged with success but it is best to remember that the first flight is full of peril. If the bird takes off on its own it inevitably lands the wrong side of the fence and will run up and down trying to get back. It will continue this procedure until you open the gate and drive it back or catch it to put it back. One can get pretty exasperated. If the first flight should be because it has been frightened it is a vastly different matter. The bird takes off in alarm and flies at great speed over the horizon. When it eventually lands it will be exhausted from the unaccustomed exercise and be lost, unless you happened to see in which direction it went and are fortunate enough to see exactly where it landed. It then becomes prey to any predator around. People with shotguns or air rifles will find it provides sport or it may quite possibly starve to death depending upon the time of the year. You have taken this bird into your life, thereby becoming responsible for its well being, so its natural instincts for survival are dormant, having food and water to hand without having to find them for itself. The right time of the year and it can manage, barring accidents, the wrong time and it will suffer unnecessarily. It is also against the law to allow into the countryside any bird that is not indigenous.

A female which, when the spring comes, has decided it is time to lay, will inevitably, should she be free flying, find that the grass on the other side is greener. If she has been accustomed to flying around the property and beyond she will choose for a nesting site somewhere off the property. Whether you can find it remains to be seen but when she comes to sit one can be sure the fox will find her and you will never see her again. Quite recently I heard of a very sad case. Having been asked to supply a drake to replace one a fox had taken, I then heard no more. This is quite a common experience and one becomes accustomed to it. People find a bird nearer home, perhaps at a cheaper price and you never hear from them again. The person in question did eventually get back to me and this time a pair was needed. The birds were housed in the garden, being shut up by night, and were full winged. At the farm next door they held regular shoots. When a shoot was to take place the farmer informed the owner of the birds and they were left shut up for the day. On this occasion when 4 o'clock in the afternoon came the owner let the remaining female out as all had gone quiet.

She took off on her usual flight and was shot. There were two new members to the shoot that day who had not been informed there were free flying domestic ducks nearby. When it was suggested that had the duck been clipped it wouldn't have happened the reply was that the owner had not got round to doing it.

The birds that choose to nest in the hedge and are left and then eaten by the fox are numerous. One is always tempted to leave a duck there, especially if the previous eggs have been clear or spoilt. A duck that is safely fenced and encouraged by suitable nest boxes to lay and sit in the house is safe.
So, in short, adequate housing, adequate fencing, adequate space.

Fencing

Should you be fortunate enough to have sufficient land to be able to fence in a sizeable area and keep your ducks out 24 hours a day you will benefit greatly as will they. Many books have explained in depth how to erect a fox proof fence but, briefly, you need a six foot fence constructed with wire netting or chainlink. The wire netting should be one inch in diameter as not only does this ensure that your birds do not go through, it is stronger and will keep out most things. The fence is best dug in at the bottom to keep birds in rather than things out for it is sensible also to use electric fencing along the outside of the main fence not only at the top but at the bottom also. I can vouch for the efficiency of an electric wire or tape at the base of the fence, nine inches away from the fence and nine inches above ground, having recently installed one myself. My dogs are miserable having had to touch it themselves to realise it is there and they are most reluctant to go down the drive which goes between two enclosures and consequently is fenced both sides. It is comical in that they proceed with extreme caution looking from side to side as if expecting the fence to leap out at them.

Blue bibbed Call female bred and exhibited by John Soper.

The electric fence would still function correctly if there was snow. If a fox were to dig down to burrow under the snow and fence he would be electrocuted when he touched the wire. A mains powered fence is a lot stronger than a battery powered one. . We do create many of the problems with foxes ourselves in that, since we have taken away their freedom and incarcerated them, our birds cannot get out, but should a predator manage to get in, it immediately goes berserk and kills for the sheer joy of it. After all, hunting in the wild is only in pursuit of one creature at a time and it is not as easy as one might think to catch that one. When faced with a whole host of potential dinners which cannot get away, can one wonder that the predator kills everything it can lay its teeth into. The fact that it cannot hope to eat everything there and then nor be able to take it all away for a later date is beside the point. The rule here is to take great care that nothing can get in.

Having erected your perimeter fence around the area upon which you have decided to put your birds, the time has come to consider the inside. Whether it is an area large enough for one pair of birds or an area designated to house six different coloured pairs all needing a separate pen I see no reason why the enclosure cannot be made as attractive as possible. Your duck runs can become a natural extension of the garden and be landscaped accordingly. It is best to protect newly planted trees and shrubs with a circle of wire netting for the newly turned earth at the bottom is fair game for dibbling beaks and the plant can be uprooted or damaged. Once the plants are established, the wire can be removed or left. A circle of heavy stones will serve the same purpose but little beaks will find a way between them if they are not put close together. Ground cover Roses, Tansy, Michaelmas Daisies, Golden Rod, Hardy Geranium, Tree Lupins etc. make a back drop to your birds, give privacy and shelter and make the duck runs most attractive. Space is needed and avoidance of overstocking, for too many birds will destroy everything you have tried to achieve. There is no reason why the duck runs cannot be an extension of the garden and an added feature of the property. To accommodate each season's youngsters a large run with little planted in it bar the odd tree for shade is to be recommended. This run will, should you have a successful breeding season, be overcrowded for part of the year and once the youngsters have been sold can be rested until the next season and allowed to recover.

Brian Bowes in Carlisle has his two ponds surrounded by a 6 foot electrified fence. Again natural vegetation provides cover and protection for his ducks.

When the time comes to cut the grass and generally tidy up care should be taken that cut vegetation is picked up and removed for, if left, it will become a hazard to the health of your birds. Cut vegetation that dies, dries and becomes wet again forms a mould which in its turn, if inhaled, can afflict the birds with a condition called Aspergillosis. This is more or less incurable and as waterfowl tend to keep their appearance and not tell you they are sick until it is very often too late to do anything about it, care should be taken to avoid the incidence in the first place. One might say that Aspergillosis is the duck's version of 'farmer's lung.'

Perhaps one of the best ways to be successful with Call ducks is to have been a breeder of wildfowl. One instinctively feels that the birds need to be kept in a foxproofed run able to live in complete freedom within the perimeters of the fence for the duration of their lives. The birds are more relaxed living uninterrupted lives with food, water and nesting facilities available to them 24 hours a day.

To be shut up is an interruption which must disrupt them somewhat. The urge to breed in all of the domestic ducks is strong and one well known breeder of wildfowl once told me, 'If you put a Mallard in the kitchen at the right time of the year it will lay.'

Sandra Barnard counting the Calls back into their night enclosure after their day on the hill feeding.

30

Water

Once the inside fences are in place and the gates constructed the pens should be grass seeded. How you are going to provide your birds with water has to be considered. A pair of Calls will thrive with a washing up bowl for water. Any sort of bowl for water is adequate providing they can immerse their heads. Obviously they enjoy life better if they can get into the water to swim and splash. Ponds can be of any shape or size and a child's paddling pool cum sand pit is ideal. These can be purchased in toy shops. I have an outlet in the bottom made watertight by an ordinary kitchen sink plug. This is ideal as it can be emptied with ease, one only having to pull the plug in the bottom, and it is strong enough to cope with general wear and tear. You will have to plunge your hand in, no matter what the weather, to find the plug but you may well find you have at least one enterprising bird who just revels in diving down pulling the plug and ensuring the next time you turn up he has a pond full of clean water. Give him a piece of string or a chain and he won't dive very far at all. If this happens a large flat stone placed over the plug ensures the water stays where you want it. These ponds are economical to buy and my oldest one is now 5 years old and has stood up to all the weather can throw at it. If you think carefully when erecting your inside fences several ponds can be sited where they can empty out into the same area via a piece of roof guttering. If this area is fenced to stop the birds from dibbling in it you can create a rather successful bog garden. The water you empty into it is rich in natural nutrients and the moisture loving plants will thrive and impress your friends and visitors alike. They then have the swimming water they love and a source of clean water from which they can drink. Swimming water must not be allowed to become so foul that it is likely to be detrimental to their well being and must be changed.

Children's sand pits are ideal as ponds. They are cheap to buy, easy to clean and give ample space for Call ducks.

Emptying the water from these ponds can be problematical in that you create a puddle of water the ducks can dibble in which shortly turns into a sea of mud. If you situate them properly you can ensure that these ponds empty outside the actual duck pen or into a central point which is fenced to keep the birds out and if you so wish this area can be turned into a feature. I have three ponds in three different runs which all empty into such an area as described above. Lengths of roof guttering channel the water where I want it thus enabling me to empty all of them daily, when necessary, in the summer. The enclosure the water runs into I have planted up as a bog garden with various primula, including candelabra, iris, primula, kingcup and mimulus. During the spring and summer it makes quite a feature and does help to keep the runs mud free.

Ponds can come in all shapes and sizes. This pond has constant running water keeping it fresh. The shingle stops the duck mess when they are paddling.

Natural water has to be the best source of all especially if it continues to run throughout the year. However it is not always easy to control, the tiniest stream turning into a raging torrent during or after heavy rain or drying up in a dry spell. Running water has a habit of washing away under fences when in flood and several predators will take advantage. Having struggled with the vagaries of a 'dear little stream' myself and the subsequent visit by the mink which follow water, not to mention the numerous rats that gained entry via the exit of the stream from the property I have to say that natural water definitely does have its drawbacks.

White Drake ('96) bred & exhibited by G & S Barnard (UK)

White Duck (adult) bred & exhibited by W Biallosterski (NL)

i

White Drake (adult) bred & exhibited by P de Bruin (NL)

White Drake ('98) bred & exhibited by P de Bruin (NL)

White Drake (adult) bred & exhibited by John Soper (UK).

White Duck ('98) bred & exhibited by G & S Barnard (UK)

White Duck (adult) bred & exhibited by C & M Ashton (UK). Champion Call Malvern '98.

White Duck (adult) bred & exhibited by P de Bruin (NL)

Grey Drake (adult) bred & exhibited by W Biallosterski (NL)

Grey Drake (adult) bred & exhibited by Carl Donner (UK)

Grey Duck (98) bred & exhibited by C & M Ashton (UK). Best of Colour at Malvern '98

Grey Duck (97) bred by Karl Fleisher (D) & exhibited by J Soper (UK)

Blue Fawn Drake (98) bred & exhibited by Alan Davies (UK)

Blue Fawn Duck (98) bred & exhibited by A Terrell (UK)

Blue Fawn Drake bred & exhibited by M Griffith (UK)

Blue Fawn Duck (19 weeks old) bred & exhibited by Tony Penny (UK)

Apricot Drake bred & exhibited by A Terrell (UK)

Apricot Duck (97) bred & exhibited by A Terrell (UK)

Apricot Drake (adult) bred & exhibited by G & S Barnard (UK)

Apricot Duck (95) bred by Tom Bartlett (Folly Farm) & exhibited by Williams & van Vliet (UK)

Pied Drake bred & exhibited by G & S Barnard (UK) Best of Colour at Malvern '98

Pied Duck bred & exhibited by Meryl Lloyd (UK)

American Pencilled Pied Drake bred (USA) and exhibited by J Soper (UK)

Silver Pied Drake bred & exhibited by G & S Barnard (UK)

Blue Silver Pied Drake bred & exhibited by G & S Barnard (UK)

Pied Drake (adult) bred & exhibited by Meryl Lloyd (UK)

AOC Pied Duck bred & exhibited by Meryl Lloyd (UK)

Dark Silver Pied Duck bred & exhibited by FC & B Millward (UK)

Black Magpie Drake bred & exhibited by FC & B Millward (UK) Best of Colour at Malvern '98

Black Magpie Duck exhibited by Williams & van Vliet (UK)

Silver Drake (adult) bred & exhibited by G & S Barnard (UK)

Silver Duck bred & exhibited by W Biallosterski (NL)

Silver Drake (97) bred & exhibited by G & S Barnard (UK)

Silver Duck (adult) bred & exhibited by John Harrison (UK) Best of Colour Malvern '98

Blue Silver Drake (adult) bred & exhibited by G & S Barnard (UK) Best non-standard colour at Malvern 98

Light Blue Silver Duck (98) bred & exhibited by G & S Barnard (UK)

Dark Blue Silver Drake (97) bred & exhibited by G & S Barnard (UK)

Dark Blue Silver Duck (94) bred & exhibited by G & S Barnard (UK)

Dark Silver Drake bred & exhibited by W Biallosterski (NL)

Dark Silver Duck (16 weeks old) bred & exhibited by Tony Penny (UK)

Dark Silver Drake (adult) bred & exhibited by C & M Ashton (UK). Best of Breed at Call Duck Experience - 98

Dark Silver Duck (97) bred & exhibited by J Soper (UK)

Dark Apricot Silver Drake bred & exhibited by Mr A J Davies (UK). Best of Breed at Call Duck Experience - 98

Dark Apricot Silver Drake (98) bred & exhibited by G & S Barnard (UK). Excellent in colour, not so good in type.

Dark Apricot Silver Duck bred & exhibited by C & M Ashton (UK)

Dark Blue Silver Duck bred and exhibited by Rosemary Sharpe (UK)

Light Apricot Silver Drake (97) bred & exhibited by G & S Barnard (UK).

Light Apricot Silver Duck (98) bred & exhibited by G & S Barnard (UK)

Blue Bibbed Drake bred & exhibited by Meryl Lloyd (UK)

Blue Bibbed Duck bred & exhibited by Mrs R Sharpe (UK)

Black Bibbed Drake exhibited by M V Hicks (UK)

Black Bibbed Duck exhibited by C Holtom (UK)

Lavender Bibbed Drake in eclipse bred & exhibited by Anne Terrell (UK)

Lavender Bibbed Duck in eclipse bred & exhibited by Anne Terrell (UK)

Pair of Penny Blacks in eclipse bred & exhibited by Tony Penny (UK)

Black Duck bred by G Jansen (NL) and exhibited by J Soper (UK)

Dusky Mallard Duck (96) bred by Karl Fleisher (D) & exhibited by J Soper (UK)

Dusky Mallard Drake bred & exhibited by A P Stanway (UK) The head colouring is beetle-green.

Dusky Apricot Drake (98) bred & exhibited by G & S Barnard (UK)

Dusky Mallard Duck bred & exhibited by A P Stanway (UK)

Dusky Blue Duck bred & exhibited by A P Stanway (UK)

Dusky Blue Drake bred & exhibited by A P Stanway (UK) The head colouring is charcoal-grey

Dark Silver Crested Drake bred & exhibited by W Biallosterski (NL)

Head shot of the Crested Duck.

Chocolate Duck bred by Claude McAlistair (USA) and exhibited by J Soper (UK). She has gone whiter as she has got older as a Black East Indian does.

Buff Duck bred by Trudi Scott (USA) and exhibited by J Soper (UK).

Khaki Drake bred by Claude McAlistair (USA) and exhibited by J Soper (UK). Should be green billed and the colour as a Khaki Campbell.

Khaki Duck (98) bred & exhibited by J Soper (UK). Close up of the laced feathers like a Khaki Campbell.

Silver Crested Duck (97) bred in Germany and exhibited by J Soper (UK)

Grey Crested Duck bred & exhibited by W Biallosterski (NL)

Butterscotch Drake bred in USA and exhibited by J Soper (UK). Should have more claret down his sides.

Butterscotch Duck bred in USA and exhibited by J Soper (UK). (Also referred to as a Saxony)

Trio of Yellow Bellies purchased recently in Holland by Tony Phillips (UK)

Note the yellow colouring developing on the underside of the female Yellow Bellies and the colour of the drake.

Yellow Belly Duck (98) bred & exhibited by J Soper (UK) from Dutch stock. The flanks show a touch of dark feathering. This should be clean of any Dark feathers.

Yellow Belly Duck bred & exhibited by G Jansen (NL).

Yellow Belly Duck bred & exhibited by G Jansen (NL).

Black East Indian Drake (adult) bred and exhibited by Paul Meatyard (UK)

Black East Indian Drake (98) bred and exhibited by Bill Nicks (UK)

AOC Miniature Crested Drake bred & exhibited by M V Hicks. (UK)

Miniature Crested Duck bred & exhibited by Sue Bray Hincliffe. (UK) Best of Breed at Malvern '98

Appleyard drake in the snow. 'Reggie' has exceptionally good Appleyard face markings, but did not hatch the correct Appleyard colour with yellow fluff and black head stripe. He was dilute Mallard colour instead. This drake often won his class and also Best of Breed. Bred and exhibited by C & M Ashton.

Appleyard ducks colour varies over the year. One bird will look best in the Autumn, another in Spring. Bred & exhibited by C & M Ashton.

Silver Bantam Drake bred & exhibited by M V Hicks. (UK)

Silver Bantam Duck bred & exhibited by M V Hicks (UK)

Silver Bantam Drake bred & exhibited by C & M Ashton (UK)

Silver Bantam duck bred by Chris and Mike Ashton. She shows the typical brown 'hood' of young females.

AOC Miniature Crested Duck bred & exhibited by M V Hicks (UK)

Miniature Crested Drake bred & exhibited by Carl Donner (UK).

Miniature Silver Appleyard Duck bred & exhibited by C Holtom (UK).

Miniature Silver Appleyard Drake bred & exhibited by M V Hicks (UK).

Graham and Sandra Barnard pictured inside their Call enclosure which is surrounded by a 6 foot fence.

A photograph of Mr. Biallostorski's ducks in a beautiful idyllic setting showing the railway sleepers which he uses to separate the ducks and also to walk over.

Anne Terrell's homestead, showing her segregated pens and natural growth of grass, trees and shrubs which give the Calls protection from the elements and aids their breeding habits.

What a difference a summer makes. Another photo of Anne's pens but this time dried out by the long dry summer.

Ponds like this are perfect for your ducks to swim, play and feed in.

An ideal setting for your ducks is an island in the middle of your stream as shown by this one at the old residence of Jane and Murray Macquaker in Northamptonshire.

Silver Bantam ducklings can be distinguished from miniatures on hatching because they have a darker brown 'hood' even at a day old, like silver Calls. The fluff on the head has a haze of dark markings over the yellow.

In contrast, miniature Appleyard ducklings of the correct colour (you can get a darker variant which looks all right as an adult) are plain yellow at day old with a strong black stripe along the centre of the head.

Chapter 3 - Feeding

The maxim for feeding should be 'the more you put in the more you get out'. One cannot expect top performances from birds if they are not fed well. There are various types of food on the market ranging from ordinary layers' pellets to specially formulated waterfowl layers' pellets. If you are keeping wildfowl then it is recommended that a special diet be fed but the Call duck is a simple creature with simple needs. Providing it can range far enough, having been given an adequate run with plenty of vegetation, it will pick up much that it needs to lay good viable fertile eggs. Add to this an ad lib supply of layers' pellets and it will do very well. Breeders' pellets can turn a bird into an egg producing machine; a bird with no surplus fat which just lays and lays. This is not the object of a Call duck. What we need is eggs with good shells which hatch. To this end if we feed layers' pellets from January onwards and through the moult, for feathers are protein and moulting time is a period of stress, and then change the diet to 50% wheat and 50% pellets, we will give our birds all that they need. The amount of wheat can be increased until the advent of bad weather. During periods of intense cold weather, protein is needed to see the bird through. Hopefully a bird will have amassed sufficient fat to help it survive. Periods of bad weather in nature sort out the weak from the strong ensuring that only the fittest survive to breed. It is a good idea to use this rule with the Calls. Providing you have maintained your bird in a proper manner there is no reason why it should not survive the severest of weather. If it does not then it was not really fit to breed from. Waterfowl belonging to the northern hemisphere naturally lay down fat to withstand the winter months and will do so on a diet of wheat and pellets. Oats are full of vitamins. Many people feed mixed corn. Far better to buy each separate type individually, it is cheaper, and you can control the amounts. Maize can be purchased nibbled which means it is cracked but as the birds can cope with whole maize I see no reason to do so as this is also more expensive and one wonders just how much goodness is lost in the process of nibbling.

During the early part of the winter barley can be fed but not too much as it will put on fat. Calls will amass fat if they are fed wheat. Barley is harder than wheat and it gives the gizzard more exercise which builds it up to maximum efficiency. The gizzard is after all a muscle. Whole maize is good to keep them warm but again not too much. One of the arguments against ad lib feeding is that the birds may become fat and suffer in consequence from heart failure. This has not been my experience for seldom do I lose a Call from anything else other than old age.

Ducks love to dabble. As soon as you put clean water in front of them, they enjoy a drink of clean water, have a swim splash the water over the sides, then proceed to dibble and make mud pies.

The food should be offered dry. Pellets rather than mash as they are less wasteful and not quite such hard work for the duck. A duck feeds for a while and then has a drink. Sufficient distance from the water means that the food does not become wet and ferment, as a consequence going rancid and endangering your birds' health. Wheat seems to be treated much as a dessert would be and they will eat it first. Seldom if ever is wheat left in the feeder the following morning but pellets will be. Care should be taken, therefore, to ensure that, despite the ad lib feeding, they have run out by the time the next feed is due, thus ensuring that all food is eaten. Young birds should have food in front of them at all times. They are growing and need to make optimum growth. A clean plentiful supply of water is also needed at all times. It can be rather daunting when a large batch of young ducklings is growing for their capacity for food seems endless and one finds that they are perpetually hungry. Eventually if one keeps increasing the daily supply there will come a time when food remains. The time has come to go into reverse and start reducing food. The birds have ceased growing at such an alarming rate. It is inadvisable to give too much food which will, if left for too long uneaten, become mouldy and stinking. Weather also plays its part where the amount of food eaten is concerned. On cold days the young ducklings will need to eat well to keep warm and grow at the same time. On warm days the amount of food taken will decrease as it will not be used to generate heat.

Ducklings which hatch and grow up in the warmer months, therefore, have a much better start in life than ducklings which have to contend with cold, wet weather. The faster a duckling is put out the better it does. Apart from the freedom and opportunity to seek natural feed as well as manufactured rations it is healthier and can develop strong muscles with increased activity. Strength and stamina increase and the bird appears to grow at a much faster rate. Early hatched ducklings are at a disadvantage if the weather makes it impossible for them to be given their freedom or if they are put out and the weather turns cold and wet. Once the growth of a duckling is checked, for whatever reason, it will be a while before it catches up. For these reasons ducklings hatched in May or later must have an advantage.

Professional pens of Calls should have proffesional equipment. This feeder is one of seven made for £6.00 by Graham Barnard after he picked up the wood at his local market. All you need is a little inclination!

If you are housing your birds by night food can be supplied inside the house. It is advantageous to have your birds leave and enter the house by a pop hole and, therefore, cut down on the food being taken by wild birds. If you are keeping your birds within a fence and out 24 hours a day the food can still be offered under cover. It is wise to keep the food as dry as possible thus ensuring that it stays fresh and is not contaminated by wild bird droppings. Mice will soon learn where the food is put and will indicate their presence by leaving droppings in the food container. I use a little house to offer food in with a board resting against the entrance. This helps to discourage crows and magpies from thieving the food, and by letting the odd shrub grow around the feeder further discouragement is given. Another board rested against the back of the feeder makes a good place to put down a supply of poison to destroy the mice. To further discourage the crows etc. a plastic bag can be hung above the feeder and in fact all manner of deterrents can be tried. It must be remembered that crows are not stupid and it doesn't take them long to figure out that if your birds are going in to feed despite your various 'scarecrows' it must be safe for them also. In fact nothing works for much longer than a week. The only way to ensure you are free from these costly creatures is to develop a programme of control.

June is the month when the young jackdaws fly and they are looking for easy pickings until they become competent at fending for themselves. If the food is out in the open the minute you turn your back they will be in and it will be gone in a very short space of time. I do advocate ad lib feeding. Birds can help themselves as and when they want. If you feed in the morning and the food is eaten by nightfall in bad weather the birds have nothing to help them withstand a night with below freezing temperatures. If you feed in the night the birds have nothing to start them off in the morning after a very cold night. If you feed twice a day they are covered but this is not always possible. I have a personal dislike of finding my birds running towards me at feed times. They are not exactly afraid of me but they really do not wish to have that much to do with me, preferring to live as natural a life, while in confinement, as possible. If they find it necessary to rush towards me when I arrive it is because they are starving and I personally feel I have fallen down on the job. I should very much loathe to have to beg for my food. Why should they?

Should you have a fish pond with duck weed growing on it and you wish to give your birds a treat, scoop off as much as you can and distribute it around the various ponds and containers. The air will be filled with dibbling noises for a very long time and the following day very little evidence will be seen that you ever put the weed out for them. The aforementioned water meadows used to supply all my needs many moons ago. The weed is teeming with pond life to provide natural protein and the plants themselves are extremely beneficial. Care should be taken that you do not fall in when collecting it or that your nine week old puppy does not mistake the green covering of the pond for solid ground. If you are like me you will grab the puppy and miss by a whisker falling in the pond yourself to end up sitting in the garden atop one of your best plants totally incapacitated with laughter. Many and varied are the hazards met when keeping Call Ducks!

Chapter 4 - Breeding Pens

There is a great temptation to pamper the best of your Calls, especially if they are successful in the show pen. While many birds that win prizes never breed, some do, but lay a reduced number of eggs. I expect at least 50 eggs per year from my birds. Four clutches of 12 eggs each. It is usually more than this for the little ducks can start laying as early as December but fertility is usually very poor if not absent altogether early in the season. Here an incubator can come in very useful in that all the early eggs can be set to find out when fertility starts. Once it has arrived one can assume that if not all eggs are fertile 99% are and I frequently transfer eggs from the duck's nest straight to a broody without testing. I am seldom let down.

Mr W Biallosterski constructed these parallel ponds using over 80,000 cobble stones which he purchased from the local council after they tarmaced the road.

I put into my breeding pens two drakes and four ducks and find, after the initial poor fertility, that I can expect up to at least 95% fertility when the season comes in proper. I allow ducks to sit themselves or indeed move a later clutch to a broody hen. I do not on many occasions bother to candle them. If in previous clutches the fertility has been good there is no reason to expect it to dwindle. While I leave my breeding birds together in their pens, other people after the breeding season split up their ducks and their drakes and house them separately. Having juggled my breeding birds about by way of adding a drake or duck or taking away a drake or duck I always leave well alone if the pen has been successful. I consider it the height of folly to interfere with a successful pen of birds. If eggs are picked up every day it would be extremely difficult to be sure which birds were laying which eggs and which ducklings one could attribute to them. For I have to admit, when one is in control, one can miss an opportunity and the odd triumph. One of the best things that happened to me was when I inadvertently necked my stock drake. With him no longer in the running I had to fall back on a son and the resultant offspring were definitely a great improvement. That, however, was a very long time ago and I am not today so timorous as not to venture forth should I think it necessary.

Occasionally one discovers that a particular drake is oversexed. This drake will favour one duck and continually harass her. He will force his attentions on her time and time again resulting in the back of her head becoming denuded of feathers. The skin will then be broken and an open wound will appear. The duck will attempt to hide herself but on every occasion she shows herself the drake will continue his harassment. Unless action is taken the duck will spend her life skulking, lose condition, cease laying and, quite possibly, the other females in the pen will be neglected and their eggs will be clear. Should there be two drakes in the pen the troublesome male can be removed and the remaining drake will cover the females with perhaps some loss of fertility. One drake only and it will be necessary to remove him or the persecuted duck to another pen returning him or her every 5 to 7 days for 24 hours. Should there be only one duck, the introduction of another female may solve the problem. These drakes are a pest and are best discarded if they display the same symptoms the following season. One can only assume that either the duck has an unusual amount of sex appeal or the drake has an abnormal number of hormones coursing through his system. There is no doubt that this phenomenon is exasperating, especially if it happens to be your only or best drake that is exhibiting it. In this instance the availability of a spare pen is very useful.

Ducks will show an absence of head feathers towards the end of the season but should not have broken skin or head wounds if the balance within the pen is right. As all domestic ducks are said to originate from the Mallard and Desmond Morris in his book 'The Naked Ape' states that the only instance of rape in the animal kingdom is committed by the Mallard, perhaps these occasional troublesome drakes are throwbacks. Harmony in the pen is to be sought at all times. Call drakes, as a rule, do not suffer from a surfeit of sexual drive but I do know of a particular pair of Khaki Campbell drakes that did. Having had an enquiry for a Campbell drake I approached a lady who I knew had two, bought as ducklings in the local market. (Buying ducklings this way is a chancy business as they are very often drakes, the breeder having sexed them at a very young age and decided to dispose of them rather than feed them if he already has plenty.) I was told she couldn't possibly part with them for they were family pets. A few weeks later she rang me to ask if any Campbell drakes were still wanted for hers had started to rape the chickens! Unfortunately they were not required.

One lady who was particularly fed up with her Miniature Silver Appleyard drake did no more than end his existence on the pretext that if she took the victimised duck away he may start on another and rang me to purchase a replacement. I have never experienced a drake going through his harem in this fashion but no doubt it is possible.

If you decide to split up your breeding birds at the end of the season it is as well to keep the ducks and drakes separate if at all possible for they are very loyal little ducks and a season spent together means that they have paired. Should you decide you want them to have different partners the following year and do not split them up before the spring approaches they will take a long time to settle. Not so many years ago I decided to split a long established pair and left it until February to do so. For an entire month the duck yelled and the drake ran the fence. That there were two runs and a drive between them did not distract them from their aim to be reunited and I confess I weakened and put them back together for the season. The following year I split them up in the summer and they did not seem to mind one bit. Ducks and drakes that have not settled produce clear eggs. While the duck lays she runs the fence as does the drake. They do settle but it takes a while and fertile eggs are lost. When I first began with my original trio of blue fawn after a couple of years I introduced a black and white duck. This duck laid more than one clutch of clear eggs and I began to despair of ever getting a duckling from her. One day while I was feeding I saw a drake approach her to mate to find that his other mates immediately interfered, no doubt haranguing him over his infidelity. Once these other mates were safely ensconced on their respective clutches the black and white duck then produced a fertile clutch of eggs and hatched them.

Should you decide to change drakes in the middle of the season I can only suggest that you wait until the ducks are all sitting to do so. The resident drake will need to be taken out of earshot and with luck the new drake will be welcome when you take their eggs away from them. Losing a drake for whatever reason during the season can be disaster for any new drake does not need to be taken from existing ducks unless they themselves are sitting. It is perhaps as well to keep a bachelor pen of spare drakes to be used in the event of a catastrophe.

I find, as mentioned above, that with two drakes and 4 ducks to a pen in the height of the season fertility is high. I have been told that 5 ducks with 2 drakes or 7 ducks with 3 drakes results in 80% fertility being good but that it can be as low as 30%. I suspect that with every increase of ducks or drakes the fertility drops accordingly. Space would also affect fertility as the more space the less chance of interference, each set of birds being able to get away from the other into relative privacy. With birds that are kept together the drakes and ducks sort themselves out and the drakes divide up the ducks accordingly. Should two birds pair, the other drake is well able to cope with the three remaining ducks and eggs are, therefore, fertile.

Choosing your breeding stock is difficult when you are presented with such a good selection as shown by this pen of whites at Graham and Sandra Barnard's.

This past year in one of my pens I suddenly realised that with all his three ducks sitting the drake was obviously bored for he suddenly took off, entered a nest box and amid much loud protest from the duck dragged her off and after pursuing her vigorously about the run, mated with her. I immediately picked him up and put him in a holding run where he mourned by the fence for some days and his ducks got on with the job of producing his offspring. He may have been upset, but they didn't miss him and were probably glad to see the back of him. It would be fair to say that young drakes can be rampant and need sufficient ducks to keep them quiet. Too young a drake with too much work to do and he may overdo things and prolapse. Once a drake has prolapsed he is useless. It is usually not difficult to become aware of this as his tackle is there hanging, not having retracted after he has mated with a duck. Should you not see this but notice a drake straining backwards as if trying to defecate this an indication that he is in trouble. Sometimes one does miss the actual prolapsing and as the member does eventually shrivel up and drop off one can find oneself with a season of infertile eggs and not be any the wiser as to why until it is too late. How many drakes I wonder have prolapsed without previous knowledge and, therefore, upset an entire season. Older drakes tend to be content with one or two ducks but, if on their own, will cope with more than two. My old man Apricot having been taken out of the breeding pen and put into the Blue Fawn run where an apricot duck was placed also took to her and her alone. That she had all blue fawn ducklings in her second clutch and all apricot in her first must prove something!

When one decides to use a particularly good drake which is small it should be remembered that if he is in a pen with ducks that are larger he is at a severe disadvantage. He may not be big enough to effect copulation and be accused of being 'no good'. In my experience few drakes, unless they have prolapsed or are sick, are infertile. It is very often a case of his being too small and thus not able to reach to fertilise the duck. Find him a duck that is his own size and who lays and he will prove his worth. Unfortunately, the smaller the duck, the better type she is and the one you wish to reproduce from may be the least likely to enable you to do so. To give the small drake every advantage it is best to choose a short duck for, come what may, he is programmed to hold the feathers at the back of the duck's head and does not realise in order to 'reach' he needs to catch hold further down the neck. Swimming water is an essential for the small drake as he has the advantage on water. It is the natural environment for ducks to mate on and also when the drake has finished and not retracted his tackle he is in a clean place. He will mate anywhere should the mood take him but to retract inside himself contaminated mud cannot be good for him. One cannot stress enough the need for clean water.

Wing clipping

One very good reason for wing clipping birds would be to prevent drakes visiting ducks of another pen and vice versa. No breeding programme can succeed if drakes or ducks are not where they are supposed to be. If one is to know with any degree of accuracy what each pen is producing it is necessary to know that the birds in each pen stay where they are put. Keeping the birds shut up until they have laid is no guarantee that you know which drake is serving which duck.

Clipping a Call's wing.

Youngsters can be pinioned by the means of a sharp blade, e.g. razor or Stanley knife, or an efficient pair of scissors. The tip of one wing is snipped off. If a blade is the chosen tool, the bird can be laid on its back on a block of wood. The aim is to remove that part of the wing from which will grow the primary flight feathers and the resulting imbalance will result in permanent flightlessness. When snipping the wing tip above the wrist joint, avoid cutting the little finger like extension of covert feathers just above it. Feathers from this section (the covert finger) will then grow out to cover the pinioned area and make it quite inconspicuous.The cut should be made just to the outside of the small protuberance which is on the front edge of the wing and towards the tip. It is preferable to slope the cut slightly inwards to ensure that no flight feathers will grow. The operation is very simple and causes no distress. It should be done within the first week of life.

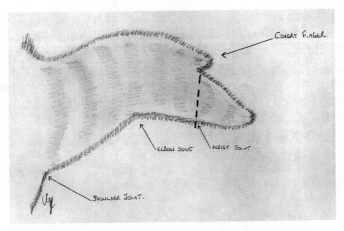

Pinioning a Call's wing

Signs to look for to ascertain commencement of laying.

Early in the season if one wishes to know which bird has started laying in a particular pen or even whether any bird is about to start to lay, signs can be seen if one studies the duck behind her legs under her tail. When she is out of lay this area slopes upwards quite sharply. When she is coming into lay it will be seen that there is a definite sagging and when she is in lay it is obvious. This is known as 'filling up', or 'filled up' meaning that she is going to lay or is laying. Another term is 'keel heavy'. It is handy to familiarise oneself with this as it saves time and energy checking nest boxes for the first eggs.

Nest Boxes

Should you decide that you wish to breed your Call ducks and not just keep them to entertain you or to bring the garden to life you will need to prepare for the breeding season well in advance. It is a good idea not to wait until the season is upon you but to be prepared from the time you first acquire your birds. If you have decided to shut the birds in overnight it will be necessary to equip the house with nest boxes. If you decide you will be picking up the eggs daily it will probably be sufficient to ensure a supply of clean straw in the house wherein the birds can lay their eggs. It is best if the eggs you pick up are clean to begin with rather than to have to wash copious dirt away. Putting dirty eggs into the incubator is to risk introducing infection which will put the whole breeding programme into jeopardy.

If you are intending to let the duck lay a clutch before picking up the eggs then you will require a number of nest boxes. As you will be taking away the first clutches of eggs either because they are infertile or because you wish the duck to lay more than one clutch, putting yourself in the duck's place would you go back to a nest box where it has been proved your eggs are not safe? Of course not, but a nest box for every clutch will not be necessary as you can move the nest box thus making her believe it is a new one.

A twenty-five litre drum with part of the end cut out makes an ideal nesting box for bantam ducks. Place a tile or something similar diagonally over the front for privacy and protection from crows and rain.

Let us assume there is just the one duck. I recommend two nestboxes put at the back of the house. They can be placed back to back facing in opposite directions or in opposite corners. In fact put them where you might yourself fancy laying an egg. Should the duck insist on laying on the floor and not in the nest box then move them and keep moving them until you have satisfied her. Should she persist in not laying in them question their suitability and change them. Call ducks are not fussy but a modicum of privacy is necessary for them to feel safe. Nest boxes can come in many shapes and forms. Cardboard boxes can be used but remember that the nest box should be stable and a cardboard box is light so put some earth in the bottom or sand to give it ballast so that when she alights on the side it does not tip towards her. A board placed beside it resting on the side of the house will ensure privacy. One of the best things to use for a nest box which is relatively easy to get hold of and is definitely cheap is a five gallon plastic drum. These used to be made of metal but, as with everything in the modern world nowadays, they are most often made of plastic. Placing the drum on its side with the bottom facing towards you and the neck of the pouring hole uppermost at the other end, cut a half moon shape out of the bottom. It is easiest to cut half the bottom away but not necessary for the Call duck can get into a much smaller hole. The reason for leaving the opening to the drum uppermost is for ventilation. Hot air rises and with this hole at the top of what is now the back of the box it can escape. You might say you have created a crude air conditioning system. Earth, peat or sand should then be placed in the bottom with a generous supply of straw. If the eggs are to be picked up each day shavings would suffice but a duck that is laying a clutch likes to cover her eggs, therefore shavings, unless they are inches deep, are not suitable. While straw has its fair share of creepy crawlies it does not have so many as hay which is not to be recommended. A brick or stone should be placed alongside the drum to ensure that it does not roll away. Once you are satisfied, a board can be put resting against the entrance at an angle. The duck will think, when she is in the box, that nobody can see her and that she is safe. Should you be troubled by Magpies, who will enter the house looking for eggs, the board over the entrance to the nest of eggs will, with luck, make them think there are no eggs present. Two of these boxes within the house will give the duck somewhere else to nest after you have taken her clutch of eggs away. Having said this, I have known a duck who has gone back to the same nest three times in a row despite twice losing her clutch. Perhaps she had remembered that the previous season she did eventually get to sit and hatch her ducklings! The reason for all this trouble is that you do not wish the duck to have to resort to laying out in the run where her eggs will be very vulnerable. Should you go to work each day and, therefore, be letting your birds out before 10 a.m. she will eventually steal her nest out of the house in the hope that her eggs will remain safe. The nest boxes are to fool her that she is doing the right thing.

Birds that are kept out 24 hours a day within a 6ft or foxproof fence suitably protected with electric fencing will need nest boxes as a permanent feature whereas the nest boxes in a house can be removed once the season has ended. Care should be taken as to where you site these boxes if there is no electric fence around the base of the fence as a duck that is sitting beside the fence may well prove too big a temptation for the fox who will dig in beside it. Should you be using 5 gallon drums these can be placed back to back around the run. It must be remembered in hot weather that plastic or metal heats up dramatically and not only will a duck be forced to desert her eggs, the eggs that have already been laid will be at risk. Again, it is quite simple to cover the box with a board or turf. The entrance to the nest box should be obscured either with a board or by facing the entrance into a bush or shrub. Again it is the magpies and crows that one is aiming to fool. Fir branches can be used to create nest sites or weld mesh placed in half moon shapes on the ground. The grass will grow up through this and create a more natural nesting site. It is best to remember when siting plastic or metal nest boxes that rain can drive into them and once in cannot get out. Should this happen the eggs will be sitting in an environment which will do them no good. The duck, if she is sitting, is likely to desert and, if laying, move to a better site. The board over the entrance serves more than one purpose. I recommend 2 nest boxes for every duck present in a run but there need be no limit to the number. You cannot have too many but you can have too few. The reason for providing nest boxes is to increase the safety of the eggs. Providing there is sufficient vegetation a duck will lay. She will lay without vegetation but she will tend to drop her eggs anywhere and once the local crow population learns there are eggs present the word goes out. Nest boxes do not mean the total safety of all eggs laid but they do ensure the safety of the majority.

It is every duck-keeper's nightmare when the enterprising crow or magpie turns up. He is going to cause havoc until he is caught. Eggs lying about the ground instead of inside a nestbox, food left lying for all to see, ducklings put out too young and just the right size for a passing bird to spot which is itself nesting and laying or rearing young and in the same need of protein as your own birds which are amply supplied with their needs by you, all help to lure in these infuriating pests. Once you have attracted the attentions of this flying menace you are going to be hard put to stop it. If you are lucky you will be able to shoot it or even trap it but until you do your losses will be great. As the raids are likely to take place early in the morning it will not be an advantage to pick all eggs up for, from the vantage point of the nearest tree, the crow will patiently wait for the duck to emerge from the nest box and then swoop down for fresh warm egg. One sees the point of all the care and attention to the making and siting of nestboxes. With the best of management one has to get up very early to thwart an egg eating crow or for that matter a duckling eating crow. The more ducklings you rear the greater the difficulties, as space inside for rearing will be at a premium and there will come a time when quite small ducklings that are off heat will have to be put out. It is these ducklings that are most at risk and which need most protection. An area covered by a plastic net can be constructed but here again care should be taken that it is secure for many a duckling has been taken from beneath a so called secure net. The more ducklings you have running about the more attention will be called to them. I have even heard of a crow taking ducklings from underneath a very realistic and painstakingly made scarecrow. As I have said before they will get used to anything given time.

Automatic watering helps to keep your ducks in good health and this one, devised by John Soper, has a catch tray underneath it and displaces any excess water outside into the pond.

Providing the duck is able she will lay eggs whether she is a pet or not. These can be taken away each day as they are laid and eaten or made into cakes. The duck will lay for as long as she cares to and then stop. Ducks usually lay by 10 a.m. and if they are kept in until this time their eggs can be secured. After a certain amount of time the duck will become determined to keep her eggs safe, probably hang on to the egg until you have let them out in the morning and then lay somewhere in the garden. It is not always an easy task locating these hidden nests. She can be kept in later to ensure the next egg is laid in the house.

Storage Of Eggs

If you decide to pick up the eggs laid daily, having left one or two eggs in the nest or nestbox to encourage the duck to return there to lay, you will then have to take care of them. They should be washed in tepid water to remove the excess dirt adhering to them and to prevent the introduction of adverse germs into the incubator. It is best to submerge several eggs at the same time so that the dirtiest can soak for a short while and remove the dirt with a sponge taking care not to destroy the natural covering of the egg. To avoid excess contamination of eggs the nestboxes should be kept as clean as possible. If the ducks are shut up every night nesting areas that are raised above floor level or into which the ducks can go will help to keep the eggs clean. These eggs should then be stored in a clean room where the temperature is constant. The kitchen is not the best place for the temperature fluctuates when cooking is in progress and the air is tainted with fumes from the oven. Also the humidity in the kitchen would fluctuate somewhat. Eggs can be stored on trays of sand on their sides. It is important to turn these eggs each day thus ensuring that the contents are not resting in the same place. Another method of storing would be on egg trays. The trays can be propped at one end on a house brick and, instead of turning the eggs, the trays can be propped at alternate ends thus ensuring the contents are resting on different sides daily. It is best not to store eggs for any length of time as their viability decreases daily. If the time is likely to pass a week and the delay in setting the eggs is due to a dearth of broodies it is probably best to set them in the incubator rather than let them become too stale. As soon as a broody is available they can be transferred after they have been candled.

The Broody Call

It has to be remembered when deciding that your Call duck will sit her own clutch of eggs that she is not to be likened to a hen. A hen that sits in the hen house, once she is fully broody can be moved to an appropriate place and resettled. One then puts beneath her the number of eggs one wants her to incubate leaving food and water within easy reach and she will happily carry on. With the duck, one must organise her somewhat. This is where the nest boxes you have placed within the fox proofed run or within the house come into their own. The duck decides where she thinks her eggs will be safe and commences to lay her clutch. In due course she sits. One cannot pick up a broody duck and move her. She must be left where she has decided, not where you want her to sit. When the time comes and you feel sure the ducklings should have hatched it is again best to leave her for you may be a day or two out and interference will cause her to desert both nest and partly hatched eggs. There are exceptions to every rule but it really is best to leave a duck to her own devices. If you are at home during the day then life is quite simple for when the time is right the duck will leave the nest with her brood usually about mid morning and that is your cue to scoop all of them up to put them somewhere safe. A duck must be allowed to be free with her ducklings. She should not be placed in a coop with the ducklings running free as one might do with a hen. A run 6 feet long by 3 feet across is sufficient, 18 inches high, with open sides, with one end covered both on the sides and on top where she can retreat for privacy and to keep dry. The food and water can be put here also but I like to put it down in the open end. Then one can observe the family.

One of the fears with all birds is that if we interfere too much they will stop laying. In the case of the Call this is not a problem but I am firmly of the opinion that if you pick up the eggs each and every day they will, in the end, give up. Much better if one lets them lay a clutch and sit on it for a day or two before one removes the eggs or until the necessary broody is available. Here I have to state that I am not a believer in mass production nor do I like artificial incubation or the rearing of masses of ducklings under lights. To me they are work which I can do without. The natural mother or a broody hen does the work for me without the continual mess and muck of ducklings dibbling away twenty four hours a day under a light.

The duck, when you take a clutch of eggs away from her, soon finds another nest site and once again lays another clutch. She will do this for anything up to five times until the middle of May when I try to ensure that she lays one final clutch and sits on this herself. My advice is to clear all nests by the middle of May, when, with luck, the duck will lay a last and final clutch. She can then be left alone to do the work herself. Call ducks make excellent mothers.

There appears to be a difference of opinion as to the exact period of time a Call duck egg takes to incubate. Having been closely associated with Calls for 21 years I have always maintained that a Call Duck egg takes 26 days to incubate. There are various factors which can influence the exact time but if I set cold eggs under a broody hen I look for the ducklings 26 days later. Weather plays a significant part in the incubation of any egg. Outside temperature can influence the exact time it takes to hatch. If a bird, duck or hen, is sitting during very cold weather, especially in the early spring, when day time temperatures are warm but result in an overnight frost, the broody bird will be hard pushed to maintain an optimum temperature overnight and until the morning temperature warms up. While this will not harm the contents of an egg it is likely to result in the hatching process being retarded.

No matter how much care we take in the storage of eggs we cannot do it as efficiently as the duck does. In actual fact we are recommended not to store eggs for too long before setting them in the incubator or under a broody hen. It never ceases to amaze me that a chicken will lay perhaps fifteen eggs and successfully hatch the entire clutch. I once had a Muscovy duck, brought home by my son, which had nested in the tool shed at the National Trust property, Cotehele House, where he was working. She must have been pretty successful in stealing her nest for she arrived together with 15 partly incubated eggs. She was deposited in the duck run and the eggs in the incubator. They hatched. I sold some, ate several and kept a drake and three ducks as they were a good lavender colour and because they would come in useful for sitting on goose eggs. I am not a lover of Muscovies and in due course decided that enough was enough and sold them at a local auction where they topped the price for that particular sale. One duck remained and she had in her nest 16 eggs. She continued to lay and I, when the opportunity arose, sneaked out a few of the eggs. She eventually sat on an unknown number. I was not worried that I would end up with yet more Muscovies for the drake was disposed of on 24th March. Possibly because I kept reducing the number of eggs she continued to lay for some time before going broody.

On the 25th May I entered the duck run to observe a duckling. Further investigation proved there were two ducklings. A Muscovy sits for 35 days. The drake had been removed 2 months before the ducklings hatched. Bear in mind the eggs I had removed and the number she laid after he had gone and one comes to the conclusion she had looked after her eggs very well!

Eggs in an incubator, unless it is a top of the range model, can be incubated at a temperature which is slightly lower than it should be or conversely slightly higher. This in itself will influence the exact time that an egg takes to hatch.

If a broody hen or duck deserts or there is a power cut, providing the eggs are far enough into the process of incubation, the eggs should not be abandoned. In fact the maxim 'Never give up on an egg' is to be advised. I have known a duck off the nest in the evening and then discovered the next morning that she is still off and the eggs appear to be stone cold. When I placed these eggs in the incubator to warm up they were found to be still alive and in fact hatched in due time. They hatched a day or two later than expected but hatch they did and the ducklings no worse for the experience. When an egg starts to cool it can be likened to hypothermia. Providing warmth is given before the life spark is extinguished the application of warmth slowly but surely brings the growing embryo back to life and it continues to develop.

One of the commonest reasons for eggs appearing to take the wrong length of time to hatch must be attributed to leaving the duck to lay her clutch and starting to count from the day we think she has gone down on them, marking the calendar appropriately. In actual fact she may have one or two more eggs to lay and we fail to notice that she is present in the run for some part of the day. We pick up the eggs and transfer them to a broody or the incubator and nothing happens when we expect it to. Candling the eggs tells us they are fertile and fully developed but as yet haven't hatched. It is sometimes difficult to decide whether an egg at full term is alive or not although an egg containing a duckling that has been dead for a day or two is very obvious because in the egg which is alive the dark line you see inside the egg is firm, whilst a line which is ragged means the duckling is dead.

One of the simplest methods to ascertain whether the contents are alive is to take a large jug or bowl of water at a temperature that one can put one's hand in and float the eggs in it. If they are alive they will quickly let you know by bobbing about. If they are near to hatching, the eggs will lie in the water at an angle and actually turn upwards from the bottom in the water as the duckling strives to break the shell. An egg that hangs suspended in the water completely still either contains a dead duckling or is infertile. It is somewhat difficult to candle eggs which a duck is sitting on for she is far more sensitive to disturbance than a broody hen. This is one more reason why it is not a good idea to let the duck sit her early clutches. Whilst it is quite possible to remove the eggs from the nest the duck is easily upset and a greater degree of management is needed.

Hatching by Incubator

To make your own candler put a full toilet or kitchen roll over a torch beam in a darkened room. You can then sit your eggs on top of the core and light will give the same effect as a bought one.

Having candled or tested your eggs and decided that hatching is to be soon, the next step is for the duckling to pierce the shell. If one looks it can be seen that a bump will appear which is an internal eruption in the shell made by the duckling. This is referred to as the egg having pipped. Then there is a pause. This pause can be of quite a long duration and it is a good idea to leave well alone. The temptation to interfere with the eggs is great, especially if they are in an incubator. Helping a duckling to hatch is a skilled job. It is perfectly permissible to give assistance, especially if an incubator has been used, for all the factors which an egg needs to hatch are not always just as they should be in an artificial environment. However, I would advise that at least one duckling should have hatched before you give any assistance and then only when you can observe that other eggs have started to hatch but have stopped.

Baby Calls are gorgeous. Evelyn van Vliet keeps hers on kitchen roll for the first few days before moving them outside. These four ducklings are only a couple of days old.

Once the egg has pipped and sufficient time for a rest has been taken the duckling will then make a determined effort to rid itself of the shell. The pipped area will be seen to extend as the duckling rotates itself within the egg, breaking the shell as it goes. Should the humidity be too low the membrane will dry too soon and the duckling will not be able to force the two pieces of egg apart. Should the humidity have been too high during incubation the inside of the egg will be sticky and the membranes will hold together, again trapping the duckling. Too high a humidity will also result in a duckling which is sticky all over and which has a large round abdomen. These ducklings do occasionally live but in many instances die. I once wrote requesting a spare part for my incubator and mentioned the problem of humidity, being not accustomed to putting any water in my incubators at all except when hatching was taking place. The reply I received from the manufacturers of my incubator was, 'You and everybody else in the country Mrs. Terrell. We suggest you put the incubator in the driest room of the house.'

Artificial incubation is a matter of experience. A machine comes together with instructions on how it works and what is recommended you do in order to hatch a batch of eggs. After that it is up to you to decide what works best for you. A person who lives at the top of a hill may in any season be hatching eggs well while a person who lives at the bottom of the same hill may be finding very few eggs are hatching. There are many factors which govern the success or otherwise of any setting of eggs. The freshness of the eggs, the hatchability of the eggs, the site of the incubator and most of all the weather. Mechanical incubation and natural incubation are dependent on the weather. Even the duck must admit defeat and start again should the elements be against her. It should be noted that a natural broody seems to have few problems with humidity. A hen sitting in a hay barn where the floor is extremely dry will hatch her eggs as also will the duck who nests in a marshy area. Both nests, one will find, are bone dry. The hen uses the humidity in the air as also does the duck who builds her nest up until it is well above the wet base. There is no real substitute for natural incubation.

However, power cut excluded, the artificial machine does not desert its eggs. Unless we inadvertently switch it off, and which of us has not over the years done that, it continues to function. The natural broody will desert for any number of reasons. There may be fleas in the nest or she may be seriously disturbed by a cat. We may shut her out by mistake or put one too many clutches of eggs under her having taken the previous ones and hatched them ourselves in the incubator. Ducks that are left to their own devices will very often come off in thundery weather or torrential rain. If they have been sitting for nearly the full length of time we can take the eggs and hatch them providing we realise that they have deserted. The reason I believe they do this is because nature tells them that should they hatch they cannot hope to rear the resultant ducklings so it is much better if they leave those eggs they are sitting on and start again. By the time the next clutch of eggs hatches the weather will have improved and they will stand a better chance of rearing the youngsters. In fact I have known ducks to desert that are already filling up and have found another nest site and are laying a further clutch within a few days. One might say this is one of the hazards of letting the duck get on with it herself. I take the first clutches away from the duck and leave her with the last clutch which usually hatches in June. This is not fool proof for the weather, even in June, can be adverse. In point of fact she does know best but what she doesn't know is that we can provide a safe environment for her babies.

Early in the season it is very often found that there is very little fertility. It seems to me that the little ducks come into lay before their mates have properly got around to thinking of producing the next generation. As well kept and well fed Call ducks will start to lay as early as January it is perhaps not surprising that the eggs are not fertile and one does wonder whether one wants ducklings in February. While rearing under a light is relatively easy, keeping them dry and warm until the weather improves enough to put them out to face the elements is a chore. This is where an incubator comes in extremely useful. The nest boxes can be cleared of all eggs laid at weekly or fortnightly intervals and the eggs put into an incubator. As the eggs are collected they are marked with the run they have come from or even with a note of the particular duck that has laid them. When they are tested for fertility it can then be ascertained which run has fertile eggs or indeed which particular duck. If you have more than one nest of eggs in each run then the colour followed by a one for one clutch on the number of eggs laid will denote one clutch, the next one being marked with a two and so on.

Call ducks are prolific layers and at least 50 eggs a season can be expected from one duck. Early in the season they can seem to go quite mad filling up a nest with up to 25 eggs and then leaving these to start again somewhere else. Many years ago I had a visit from a student at Bristol University who re-quired 5 pairs of Call ducks with which to complete a project His aim was to put a pair to a pen in a building (I cannot imagine the noise level in an enclosed space should they all decide to call at once) and then test their blood for hormones. They were to be tested before they laid, when they laid, when they sat and when they were rearing. I never heard the end of the story but I did get a frantic phone call asking me how he could get them to stop laying and sit for one had 25 eggs in her nest and was showing no signs of going broody. I couldn't help him a lot for I have never discovered how to manage the little ducks if they didn't want to be managed. Part of the joy of Calls is the fact they have minds of their own and we can but strive to creep up on them by devious means to get out of them what we require.

This batch of Calls belonging to Anne Terrell has one or two which, even at this early age, look excellent.

Having allowed your duck to lay either several clutches or taken her eggs away every day or every two or three days, the middle of May is the time to let her sit herself. She should then be allowed to get on with it. Extra vigilance is needed to ensure that you have some idea of where she is laying and at what stage she has begun to sit. It is a good idea to jot it down on the calendar and make a note 26 days in the future which bird is to hatch when. Strange notations appear on my calendar e.g. B.F. Corn. Haz. Translated this means Blue Fawn in the corner where the Hazel bush is as opposed to the Blue Fawn in the corner by the tree lupin. A.B.C. Gal. is Apricot near the galvanise.

Having placed your first harvest of early laid eggs in the incubator you can then, after a few days, test them for fertility. If the birds have come into lay particularly early there will very often be no fertile eggs or perhaps only one. I have to confess that nowadays I do throw away the first eggs and only set the next harvest. It will be found with each successive setting that fertility increases and it is safe to say that when you are getting about 50% fertile these are the freshest eggs you have picked up and that fertility has arrived.

Now is the time to leave the eggs in the nest and allow the duck to lay her clutch. A clutch consists of between 10 and 20 eggs. The duck will lay 3 eggs before she begins to cover them when she leaves the nest box. This is a cry back to the wild where ducks lay the first few and test the safety of their nests. If the first eggs are taken by a crow or other predator, the nest site is not safe so she must find somewhere that is. If you are picking up the eggs as they are laid it is as well to leave an egg or two or the bird is going to be searching for a safe site and will then become very discouraged. When she is approaching the conclusion of her clutch she will begin to line the nest with down. When down is first noticed there are 2 or 3 eggs left to be laid and the duck will then commence to sit. Now it is time for you to decide whether you are to let her sit herself or whether you are to remove the eggs to put them under a broody hen or into the incubator. Having been allowed to lay her clutch and to begin sitting, she will, if you take her eggs away, begin to search for another nesting site that is safe and lay the next clutch. She will do this for 3 or 4 times depending on the level of your management.

Eggs can be picked up as they are laid but while the duck seems to be able to keep 18 eggs in top condition with the first eggs being as viable as the last we cannot hope to be so lucky and the eggs must be set within a few days. To do this, adequate incubator space must be available together with optimum storage. If you let her lay a clutch and sit on it for 10 to 14 days she will have completed the most difficult part of the incubation leaving you to complete it.

This can be done by removing the eggs to an incubator or to the care of a broody hen. Call duck eggs are not the easiest to hatch and every chance must be given for them to do so. If you have a top of the range incubator especially designed and proven to be ideal for hatching waterfowl eggs then so be it but most of us are destined to use the more run of the mill machine and our chances are not quite so high. Therefore it is probably best either to allow the duck to incubate the better part of the time and remove the eggs to hatch in the incubator or take the eggs away when a broody hen is available. Unless the hen is very badly mismanaged she will do the better job. It should also be remembered that waterfowl eggs do not hatch quite so spontaneously as hen eggs. A hen's egg seems to no sooner pip than it is hatched. Waterfowl eggs will tap for a very much longer time and then the duckling will rest. One particular hatch which was set under a broody hen proceeded as follows.

Monday - Tested in water - bobbing well but not turned.
Tuesday - Checked in the evening, faint tapping heard.
Wednesday - Tapping strongly.
Thursday - Pipped.
Friday - Starting to go round in the morning.
Saturday - Hatched.
Sunday - Put out with broody hen.

The temptation to help a duckling to hatch is overpowering. Speaking to a fellow breeder of Calls I was informed that he no longer helps any ducklings out of the shell as he hasn't the time. Those of us with the time will be hard put to it not to. There can be no doubt that unless the duckling is having trouble hatching due to the faulty incubation of the egg, to help it is to create a strain of birds with poor hatchability. Hatchability is a fact of life and different strains of birds have different success rates. The coarser the Call the easier it is to hatch. The better the Call the more difficult. Being successful with good Calls is extremely difficult.

There is some skill in deciding when to actually clear the nests in May, as, if you leave it too long, a bird will decide enough is enough and you will not get that last clutch. However, it does not take many seasons for you to be able to judge whether to leave a duck or take her eggs away to achieve that last clutch. I must confess here to wanting my birds to be able to sit and hatch their own. They have done their best for me as I have for them for three to four months and somehow I feel it is only fair that they should be given their reward. If I do my stuff they are successful despite what nature throws at them and while there is a fair amount of time and work involved there is nothing to match the sight of a mother duck with her brood.

Rearing

If you have hatched your ducklings under a broody hen or duck you will need to make alternative arrangements unless you have decided to use the natural broody just for hatching and you intend to take the ducklings away and rear them yourself. I have to admit that this is a much safer way to ensure the safety of your ducklings, especially if the weather is wet. A broody hen in a run on the lawn is hard pushed to keep her ducklings dry and if they become wet and chilled when first put out they will die. What I use is a tunnel greenhouse. Man did not create the tunnel greenhouse for anything other than the rearing of waterfowl of any description. Mine is 10ft wide by 20ft long but they come in varying sizes so you can decide for yourself just how big a space you will need. The greenhouse provides an ideal environment for rearing. It gives the maximum of light and is entirely dry. Its one drawback is that it does become very hot when the sun shines and very cold during the night when there is a frost about. When it becomes very hot the hens can cope with the heat and young ducklings revel in it. A duck that is in there at the time does not cope so well and under no circumstances must she run out of water. If the hot spell turns out to be of any length of time all one has to do is open the pen and let mother and babies out. Providing they are over the first week of age they are big and strong enough to roam with mother for protection. If the greenhouse is situated within a stockproof fence the mothers and babies can roam at will until such time as they are big enough to be transferred to the main pens.

My greenhouse is divided up into pens three foot square which gives adequate room for the average brood. I do have one or two bigger runs which will accommodate ducklings that have been reared under lights which no longer require heat but are not quite big enough to be transferred to the main pens. A short stay in the greenhouse followed by some time roaming free around it being able to retreat to the shelter of the greenhouse and to go back there to feed ensures they are safe until they are transferred to the main duck run. It is also a bonus for me for I can see them from the kitchen window and hear them if and when they get into difficulties. No matter how hot it becomes they do not desert, merely lifting when the temperature is highest and opening their beaks to dispel the heat. It never ceases to amaze me but I have never had one desert her nest and so long as the eggs are fertile they rarely fail to hatch.

The 'brooder house' at Anne Terrell's.

Into each pen I put a dish of chick crumbs together with a portion of wheat. The drinker I put on a block to raise it above the level of the shavings which cover the floor. This helps to keep the drinker clear of debris. I feed and water the ducklings twice a day visiting new batches at least once after they have first been moved. Usually, when I go back to check, all I can see is the hen with the brood safely under her. Occasionally I go back to find ducklings huddling together and mother has escaped. Sometimes I find mother there and the ducklings have escaped. No matter how careful you are it is always best to check. The more precious the brood the more likely a mishap whether it be under a light or under a broody mother.

The greenhouse not only helps to keep them safe but they are all under one roof. Feeding and watering and cleaning out is done in the dry even if it is tipping with rain outside and it is a pleasure to stand and survey the new arrivals. The transition from run to the outside world is done gradually with the mother making up her own mind when to lead her babies out and one avoids taking them from a restricted space to an enormous area that must be rather bewildering. With food placed outside the runs in the space down the middle it is easy to find, and shallow containers outside provide easy access to drinking and swimming water. If necessary they can all be driven back into the greenhouse if the weather turns foul and they are getting wet (a thing that rarely happens because the mothers, duck or chicken takes them back herself) or because I wish to have a closer look at them or catch the odd one.

Artificial rearing from day one.

Once the ducklings have all hatched and within a few hours they are completely dry, it is time for them to be moved on. If you have hatched just a clutch of perhaps 10 to 12 ducklings, a cardboard box is quite sufficient to start them off in. I personally use electric light bulbs of 60 watts. It is not economical to use an infa red lamp of a great wattage for a small brood. Line the bottom of the box with a plastic feed bag and put into it a layer of shavings 2 to 3 inches deep. Should you have the box in the house it will not be long before water starts to seep through the bottom. Add to this a container filled with chick crumbs and a receptacle with water. Water should not be given in an open container for ducklings should not become wet.

Having been hatched in an artificial medium they are not waterproof. One advantage the ducks gives her ducklings is that all the time she is brooding them she is coating them in a layer of oil from her own plumage which will safeguard them when they take to the water for the first time. Gather your ducklings from the incubator putting them into a large jug or bucket and transport them to the box. After you have placed them there spend a few moments observing them and then walk away. If you return in about half an hour you will have a fair idea as to whether they are warm enough or not. If they are piled on top of one another beneath the light they are cold and conversely if they are stretched out around the sides of the box they are hot.

The way to regulate the heat is simply to raise or lower the height of the electric bulb. If you find it impossible to keep them warm then reduce the area that they are in and place a towel over the top of the box leaving one end open to allow the hot used up air to escape. Your ducklings will live in this small world for several days but in a very short space of time will become messy, smelly little demons demanding that you keep adding and adding yet another layer of shavings to keep their home dry. The time has come to move them into a larger area and, as they will be over the first tender days, while they will still require warmth, they will not need quite so much of it. It is a good idea to have an area which can be used for the next step and a further area where they can live off heat for as long as it takes them to grow big enough to go out into the wide world if the weather allows. While water is essential to them it can be a nightmare also for they love to play with it as well as to drink it. The area around the drinker will become saturated and must be kept clean for it does the ducklings no good at all to become wet and not be able to dry off in a fairly short time.

Hence the necessity to house them in a area big enough to be both wet and dry at the same time.

Ducks grow very fast and it is not long before feathers will appear on the shoulders of your ducklings. Now is the time to change their diet from chick crumbs to growers' pellets. This should be done as a gradual process, placing growers' pellets in the food container and covering them with chick crumbs. In a very few days they will be clearing the dish and not eating the chick crumbs. For the duration of their stay indoors, water that is in a suitable drinker should be offered. Open bowls of water are an invitation for them either to get severely chilled and catch pneumonia or just to make the whole area they inhabit into a quagmire.

Once you have decided that the ducklings are big enough to be placed outside and that the weather is favourable, providing they have developed the feathers on their breast, a shallow bowl of water can be provided and you can stand back and watch the fun for they will play and swim and generally have a lovely time. Do ensure that the container is shallow and is easy to get out of. A brick or small ladder is always advisable.

Many a duckling has been found dead in the water container. There is nothing quite so devastating as to realise you have been the cause of its death through lack of thought and that all your hard work has come to nothing due to a small hiccup in detail. Beware the surrounds of the drinker for it will become muddy in a very short space of time and the drinkers will need to be moved frequently to ensure that the whole of the run does not become a mud pit. Once I consider the growing birds are big enough or the area around the greenhouse is becoming over crowded I move them down to the main run. Here they have a much bigger pond to swim in and they are big enough to get on and off without any worries on my part. Food is provided under cover and as there are nearly always other birds already in residence I do not have to worry that they will not find it. As these pens tend to hold quite a few ducks it is necessary to change the ponds, which are children's sandpits or paddling pools, at least every other day if not every day. It very much depends upon the number of ducks and the weather.

A lot of ducks and they are changed every day because they become very foul and in hot weather they simply go off and the smell reaches you from quite a distance. I have been known to change ponds twice a day in extreme temperatures. Clean water is more important than food. One only has to witness ducks hanging about as you empty the pond and then to see the delight they express when they can get onto it. I have seen one of my ponds so full of ducks enjoying clean water that every so often one or another is swept over the side by the enthusiasm of its friends. It has to turn around and jump back on.

Vigilance is the order of the day for newly hatched ducklings are vulnerable. Crows and Magpies relish ducklings and rain can kill them in a short space of time. While ducks like to have water underneath them they are not so happy with water pouring down on top of them. Cold and wet must be the biggest of all the killers of newly hatched and growing ducklings. As soon as you see the mother and ducklings out of the box in the run then is the time to pick them up and put them where they will be safe.

It must be remembered that ducks do not brood their offspring in the same manner as a hen will so, wherever they are put, make sure that, should it rain, they remain dry. I cannot think of a better sight than mother and ducklings going about their business in the duck run on a sunny day.

Anne Terrell's ducks have fresh water every day and their ponds, which are children's sand pits, are changed every other day. The overgrown area in the middle is where all the old water is drained off to. This turns it into a marsh like area, which grows some wonderful plants.

It is very tempting to leave them but don't unless she is the only duck present. Call drakes as with Mallard drakes are unreliable parents. He will play with the ducklings if the mood takes him tossing them about with inevitable results. There is nothing much of the proud father about a Call drake. If there are other ducks in the run the mother duck will drag her brood about never giving them time to rest or feed and eventually they will die from cold, exhaustion and hunger. Much better to scoop the whole boiling of them up and put them somewhere safe. I have known Call ducks to lay 12, incubate 12, hatch 12, rear 12 and then, providing it is early enough in the season, do it all over again. It is not so easy for this to happen today for the standard of the Calls has improved out of all recognition over the years and hatchability has to some degree been lost. I well remember having 12 ducklings hatch in November and what a nuisance they were to rear. Much better to hatch and rear at the proper time of the year, for keeping the ducklings warm and dry however or wherever is nothing short of a nightmare.

There is a theory that late hatch ducklings are the ones to be sought after, they are smaller than early hatched ducklings. I cannot agree as to my mind it all depends on the meshing of the correct genes as to whether a duckling is to grow up fit for the show pen and a world winner rather than on the time of the year it is hatched. In my opinion show standard Calls arrive at any time of the year and if they are destined to be small they will be. One might even say the advent of show standard Calls rests in the 'lap of the gods'.

Grading for Breeding & Culling

There is absolutely no need to sex Call ducklings manually as, given time, they will resolve the problem for you. It is quite simple. The ducks quack, and can they quack, and the drakes don't. Drakes have a curl in the tail. Should you still be wondering, the drakes will colour up into their adult plumage eventually. However, given time, you will be able to get the feel of your ducks and be fairly certain what sexes you have long before this. I have to admit that I can now look at a brood of ducklings when they are quite small and be pretty sure how many drakes there are. They do fool me with a smaller one on occasions which I am sure is a duck and it then turns into a rather nice drake. You will probably hatch more drakes than ducks. At one time it was particularly difficult to hatch a good drake and I encouraged indigestion by stating that I would eat my hat if a particular duckling wasn't a drake. It was and when I look at him today I can see just how far the Calls have improved in the last eight or nine years.

Most of us want to know what we have hatched and we also want to know how we can achieve sexing. It is a very simple matter to vent sex the ducklings at a fairly young age. If you are used to the process and have good eyesight they can be done any time after 3 days when the yoke sac inside the duckling has been fully absorbed. Take your duckling, turn it upside down and with the thumbs of both hands gently open the vent. If it is a drake its penis will pop out with a little pressure. This is very easy to recognise for it gives the appearance of a bean shoot. If there is no bean shoot and you open the vent further and find nothing then you have a duck.

As there are few seasons when we are fortunate enough to hatch more ducks than drakes we must decide what we are to do with them. Personally I separate off the drakes that I do not need and when they have acquired their adult plumage I cull them. A Call drake weighs approximately one and a quarter pounds. Plucked and dressed they make an excellent meal and are delicious. I rarely get to sample one nowadays for people have discovered this fact and I can sell every one, always having to disappoint every year. They are ideal for an old age pensioner who would find buying a duck for the table very expensive and will possibly do two meals. I am afraid we eat one each and relish every mouthful.

For people who cannot keep a Call duck because neighbours are in too close a proximity two drakes are the answer. They look good when in their full colour, make little noise, bring the garden alive with their presence and eat the slugs and snails. I must stress that the problem of excess drakes is an annual one and it is best to decide on the course to be taken and stick to it. The male Call duck is just the same as the male pig, sheep or cow, he is surplus to requirements and has to be dealt with.

I have very strong views on the subject of culling surplus stock and am well aware that not everybody agrees with me, nor is everybody able to cull when necessary. It is my opinion that before keeping any creature which one has the intention of breeding and thus producing more of, that one should, before doing so, look to the future and examine the fors and againsts. Even if one is only to reproduce for one's own flock one is going to end up with more than can be coped with or indeed than there is space for. Therefore, before breeding, it is as well to examine the amount of space available. It is a fact of life that probably there will be more males than females and also a fact of life that they are going to be a problem to dispose of.

The drakes that end up in my drake pen are in most cases destined for the table. Occasionally one is sold for breeding purposes but should the drakes left be large, coarse, of poor type or mismarked, they are culled. It is a wise precaution to reserve for one's own use spare drakes as, if you lose your stock drake at the wrong time of the year, you are not going to be able to replace him with a bird that will enhance your flock. Unless you have just started you are unlikely to be caught without a duck for most of us run more than one duck but do not necessarily keep more than one drake. In a pen with four ducks and two drakes we can get by with one drake but perhaps at the cost of a little fertility. Having a spare drake available may just be the salvation of an otherwise disastrous breeding season but we do not need half a dozen spare drakes of one colour. Apart from spare drakes we are occasionally going to have that bird which has damaged itself or that is ailing and needs to be culled. There is nothing worse than visiting a collection to observe a cripple eking out an existence. People express varying degrees of surprise when I suggest that they eat their spare drakes. Either they are horrified and claim that they could never eat the dear little ducks or they have never given the matter a thought. Let me tell you that Call Duck is delicious. Roasted in a pan on a grid, smothered in salt, or if you are worried about your blood pressure, smeared with honey, they are lovely and the skin crisps beautifully.

I very often cull upwards of 30 drakes per season. If I didn't we would soon be overrun with standing room only. Putting them in the local market can be the answer or selling two drakes to people who yearn to keep the little duck but who have to consider neighbours. The latter it has to be said is a limited market and cheap ducks bought in the local market are not always looked after as one might wish, for having spent so little on acquiring them, it is not all the world if the fox eats them. Much better if we know the end of our surplus drakes rather than dispose of them any which way we can. It is far too easy to have a successful season and then panic. It must be realised that it does no good whatsoever to flood the area with cheap birds of substandard quality. It does the breed no good and does one's reputation no good either. Often have I had an enquiry for a drake to be told my price is too high. My usual reply is that the caller has called the wrong place. I value the product I produce.

It is no disgrace not to be able to cull although it is better if one learns how to do the job properly. There is always going to come a time when a bird is suffering and is better put out of its misery. When this happens it is handy,if you are unable to do the job yourself, to know a person who can. I have a husband who is my executioner. I pass sentence and he carries it out but if the need arises I am capable of doing the job myself for I cannot bear the thought of a bird suffering unnecessarily. We also run a service whereby people with surplus males can put them in a box, call and leave the box behind. The birds are dispatched humanely and disposed of. Tuition is given if required and so many people experience real relief when they find they are no longer wondering how to solve the problem of surplus males that they realise that culling is truly necessary, especially when the cost of the feed bill drops.

My first season with the Calls produced 13 ducklings, 10 ducks and 3 drakes. Perhaps this was an ill omen if one is suspicious of the number 13. I have been beset by the little beggers for more than 20 years and still they have not lost their appeal. That first season did not foretell the future for it is the only time I have produced more ducks than drakes. In some years one has more ducks than drakes in a particular colour but overall it is almost a certainty there will be surplus drakes. I use five pens to house my youngsters. The area around the greenhouse is used to see them up, fully feathered and running. When they are moved onwards they are sorted. Spare, big and ugly drakes are put into the large pen which also houses the Miniature Silver Appleyards bred for the year. Into another pen go the Apricots. There tend to be a lot of these for I do admit to concentrating on them. Blue Fawns together with Bibbed, Mallard, White, any Apricots I particularly want to keep my eye on and lately Black in another. I put Lavenders together with any Blue Fawn I do not wish to lose sight of and the odd Apricot I do not wish to mix up with the others in another. Once the birds are in their final runs I do stand a chance of having some idea of what I have as while they are spread around the property it is all too easy to forget the odd one of a particular colour. While I do not pretend to know the parentage of every bird, I can, by separating the colours and using these pens to keep my eye on the ones that interest me, keep track of particular broods. The late hatches are left around the greenhouse. It is interesting that as these usually have the duck with them the same ducks appear year after year. As one can create a strain that starts to lay late with few eggs in a season, so one can create a strain that not only lays early in the season but, with careful management, will still be laying late in the season. One should be very careful not to pursue a line of breeding which will end with the production of a limited number of eggs. The same rules apply when dead in the shell becomes a problem. While we can inbreed for a while there comes a time when extinction is around the corner if new blood is not introduced. On occasions this can cause a new set of problems as well as curing the old. We may find that the standard of our birds decreases but once we have produced new females these can then be put back to our own drakes and hopefully for a few years at least the spectre of dead-in-the-shell will be eradicated.

Chapter 5 - Colour Breeding

This is not a chapter on the various colours that one can expect to find in Calls for one has only to read the Standard to ascertain what colours are in fact standardised and what colour pattern is asked for when breeding a particular colour. I am about to try to give a summary of what colours to expect from particular colours put together in a breeding pen and what colours to avoid together in a breeding pen.

When asked to write on colour I expressed the opinion that I was being asked to step into a minefield for I suspect whatever view I express whether from experience or deduction there is someone somewhere who will not only tell me I am wrong but prove me to be wrong. I will try to keep the following paragraphs as lucid as I can and can only advise that should you become hopelessly confused you cease reading and go out and prove for yourself the facts and fictions of colours in Calls. I am not an expert on genetics never having studied them. Each time I come across an article on genetics I cravenly pass it by. While I do not doubt my ability to understand, I lack the resolution to apply myself. Over the years I have unconsciously accumulated a fund of knowledge which while writing this screed I have dredged up from the recesses of my memory.

Wild Mallard as illustrated in the book 'The Waterfowl of the World' by Jean Delacour (1964) come in various mutations and since they were first kept in captivity probably several centuries B.C. the various mutations have been fixed by selective breeding among captive birds. If one studies the colour plate depicting 6 colour mutations of the Mallard one can see that the Call does no more than follow these mutations. If one studies the colours of the various forms of domestic ducks it can be seen that the Call also follows these. Given time, I see no reason why we should not eventually have all the various colours depicted by the tiny Call duck. In the meantime, however, we have standardised a limited number of colours, these being white, mallard, blue fawn, apricot, pied, silver, dark silver, magpie and bibbed. All of these should breed true as they are standardised. Over the years mutations have occurred within these colours, usually due to cross breeding. We now find ourselves to have a super abundance of 'any other colour'. Care I believe must be taken that we do not become swamped in new colours to the detriment of the standard colours. It is difficult enough to breed the true colours to standard without embarking on a whole programme of new colours. Moves have been made to standardise many of the new colours but in some instances care should be taken for having standardised the Magpie Call we now find that there are very few left in existence. Standardising the Magpie Call was easy for all that we needed was to state that both male and female should have colour and markings as for the large Magpie ducks. Before a colour is standardised I believe that it should have been proven to breed true for 10 years and to do so in the hands of several breeders. To standardise a colour only to find within a short time it ceases to exist is pointless. If a colour is bred by a limited number of people it is far too easy for this colour to be lost from either predation by foxes or from passing the birds on to what are thought to be safe hands to be bred and improved. Once a strain is lost it is not easy to find again for so often it happened by chance in the first place. This was the fate of the Magpie Call. The original cross which produced Magpie Calls was a Black Bibbed duck to a Pied drake. The resulting offspring were white, black bibbed, pied, magpie and mallard with pale throats. Each of these would be split for colour with everything else!

I have been unable to find any correspondent who could contribute further on the matter of colour. Today, more standardised colours do breed true than when I started in 1977. The reason for this is that in the 1960s Jack Williams, an expert in the breeding of wild geese, seeing and taking a fancy to Calls imported them on two occasions from Holland. These were white, silver, mallard, blue fawn and pied Calls. In his first breeding year they did not breed very well. After importing more the following year he was taken ill and had to go into hospital before he had sorted his Calls into their breeding pens. They all, therefore, remained as a flock with all the colours mixed. Fertility and hatching were very good and he reared in the region of 150 birds. Of these only a handful were odd coloured. I saw some of the progeny of these on 16th October, 1977 at a B.W.A. Open Day at the Collection of Jack Williams in Norfolk and acquired a trio of blue fawn in the same year. I had seen numerous Calls previous to this but nothing to match the quality of these. The following season I bred them to find I had in the offspring not only blue fawn but white, mallard, silver and apricot. The only thing I lacked was pied! Having stuck to the same line all these years my blue fawn stock birds will still on occasions breed all of these colours although over the years white and silver have declined. The silver I bred then did not resemble the silver bred today. The ducks were much whiter with markings while the drakes did not have quite as much mulberry on their flanks, more nearly resembling the mallard. The Apricot as we know it today was then referred to as the Apricot Blue and I firmly believe that, had we retained this name, the confusion experienced today would not have arisen. Falling in love with the colour of the apricot I started to specialise with the result that today my apricots do breed apricot with the very occasional white.

A breeding pen of White Calls at Anne Terrell's under the careful eye of her German Short-haired Pointer bitch, Solace.

The standardised colours should breed true. If there is any other colour behind them this will occur on occasions. One should always, when finding an odd duckling, take into account the meshing of the various genes and the hatching of every egg. Many a rash statement is made. Once being told that a particular pair of birds always produced females I enquired somewhat later in the conversation how many of these particular birds had been bred. The answer was two!

White Calls should breed white Calls. One of the clues as to whether a white is not pure can be seen in black markings on a bill that should be a clear bright orange-yellow. White Call ducklings when they first feather up can have the odd black feather which disappears when the first moult is over. If there is some other colour way back in the pedigree this can come out many years later and totally take one by surprise. However, it is always as well to consider whether a roving drake has gained access to the breeding pen without our knowledge. I was astounded one year after hatching a yellow duckling with dark points as never before had I experienced this. Some weeks later when it had grown into a light mallard coloured stocky duck I remembered I had found my Miniature Silver Appleyard drake in the pen one morning. He had obviously been there long enough to make his presence felt.

The colour white is recessive and, therefore, handy to prove the pureness of colour. If you breed a pure colour to white the resulting offspring will be all coloured i.e white to mallard, the offspring will be mallard, white to a mallard carrying white, the offspring will be 50% white and 50% mallard. A clue as to whether a bird is carrying white can be seen when it has a pale area under its chin which represents a colour fault in a standardised colour. Colour to white produces all coloured ducklings providing the colour is pure.

The birds with an eye stripe i.e blue fawn, apricot and mallard can be interbred to produce blue fawn, mallard and apricot. Providing each of them is a pure colour or has itself derived from the eye stripe brigade they will have pure markings. Again one must be sure no other colour is lurking within awaiting discovery.

Mallard to blue fawn - 50% of each
Apricot to blue fawn - 50% of each.
Apricot to mallard - 50% of each
Mallard to mallard   - mallard
Blue fawn to blue fawn - blue fawn
Apricot to apricot   - apricot

The bibs come in three colours i.e. black bibbed, blue bibbed and lavender bibbed. Bibbed to bibbed will produce bibbed and white. Putting black to black, blue to blue and lavender to lavender you will get predominently black, blue or lavender. Make up any combination and the results will vary with white as a bonus.

Self Colours

From the bibs it is possible to produce a Call that is self coloured. To this end a breeding programme was undertaken in 1993 to produce a self coloured black. Black bibbed were selected which had no white flights and the minimum amount of white on their chests. These were bred together to produce a bird that displayed very few white feathers. The type was appalling and a good type mallard was introduced to improve it. This was to prove a grave mistake for all blacks now display mallard marked feathers either on the breast or under the tail. In some cases both. To date, while some self black birds are produced, a large number of mallard and bibbed also occur. It will take time to produce a bird that will breed true.

A White Call female, bred in 1994 by Tony Penny. She was Show Champion at Devon County Show 1998

I myself have produced a self coloured lavender duck without even trying, having four fertile eggs from my lavender duck which came via a white bird with a black bill produced from a pair of blue and white pied (mother and son) put to an apricot drake. Having despaired of ever producing from this black billed white which we called 'the coloured white' anything with her excellent type it was suggested to me that I try her to Apricot. To my utter surprise I produced not only white birds but lavender. Bearing in mind that the head of an apricot drake is pale grey or lavender perhaps I should not have been surprised for she herself was carrying the colour gene for blue and from it, therefore, followed lavender. One can look back and see the logic but at the time it did not occur to me to put this duck to apricot. I have never since produced anything from these offspring but lavender, white and the occasional apricot. Acquiring some black Calls, I put with them one of my lavender drakes with the minimum of white on his chest. This year I produced an apricot duck with a black bill. The old coloured white has gone to meet her maker. Do I start to call this bird the coloured apricot?

The four fertile eggs from the coloured white and apricot's daughter sired by an apricot pied drake were put under a Falcated duck she being the only broody I had available at the time. In due course I discovered four duck-lings swimming on the pond and with great reluctance took them from her to rear myself. I am not sure when I first realised that I had a duckling which looked as if it might fledge all one colour. I do know I waited with bated breath for the advent of the flight feathers and was duly amazed when they too were seen to be lavender. The only white she had on her was a tiny patch under the chin. Alas after nearly 30 years of keeping my birds safe, a fox dug in under the fence and that was the end of the foundation of a dynasty, thus illustrating the fact that until a new colour is firmly estab-lished in several collections, breeding true and thriving, thought should be taken before it is standardised. I have several lavender bibs with very small bibs but no self coloured bird has reappeared.

Controlled breeding for a colour cannot be a bad thing. Indiscriminate breeding of colours cannot be justified. It has taken a very long time to begin to bring the colours to the point when they will breed true with few other colours in the clutch. There is a question mark over the selling of a bird that is not going to produce that same colour. Having brought in a drake as an outcross only to find he threw just about anything one cares to mention put my breeding programme back when he should have furthered it. It is unfair to the serious breeder. Many people delight in the uncertainty of what they will find when the eggs have hatched, others experience a considerable set back. However one soon becomes familiar with breeders who breed birds that will produce the colour one wants. If one talks to various people one gains the knowledge needed to decide where to go when one wants an outcross.

In years past the birds that hatched which did not conform to the colour standard were referred to as any other colour (A.O.C.). The breeders at that time found it very difficult to sell them and indeed these birds were often destroyed. People preferred to buy a bird that was a standard colour rather than one classed as any other. Placing them in the local market did find them a home for people there buy what they see rather than a particular type or colour. With the advent of these birds beginning to breed true, names are being given to the colours, thus promoting them from obscurity. I see no reason why these colours cannot, given time, reach colour status but let us not be too hasty.

Trees provide cover from direct sunlight in the summer as shown by this white Call of Evelyn van Vliet.

One of the most popular colours is the apricot and demand is usually high for these birds. After the classes at the shows and auctions, apricots are the most numerous. As stated above, in my early days the apricot was referred to as the apricot blue meaning that the bird was an apricot shade with blue shading on the crown of the head and over the back. The blue fawn was referred to as the blue and the blue markings on it are duplicated in the apricot. Hence the blue and the apricot blue. The flights and speculum were also blue. Today, birds which are not apricot are being put into the apricot classes at shows. The characteristic eye stripe is missing and the colour is more buff than apricot. Putting a bird such as I have described in an any other colour class at a show I was asked why, for it was apricot. The person who enquired was either not familiar with what an apricot should look like or had, noticing that the bird was orange in colour, assumed it was an apricot. There has been some dissatisfaction at shows where birds that have won previously have been transferred to an any other colour class. A pity that the owner had not studied what he had before complaining. More and more of our judges are studying colour as, with the advent of so many new ones, there is a great need for vigilance. Also, newcomers to the breed, if told the bird they have bought is a certain colour, do not know any different. To summarise the above, each colour should breed true. If in past generations there has been an introduction of any other colour this may result in the offspring being of varying colours other than the colour of their parents. With the meeting of the right genes past generations can turn up many years after the original introduction. Perhaps I should have confined myself to this statement at the beginning and stopped with the same!

Crested Calls

When are we ever satisfied? It is not in the nature of man to be ever truly satisfied and no more is it in the breeding of Calls. Whether we seek to breed a better Call of a particular colour or seek to breed something new, we are for ever looking for yet another diversion and to this end a determined effort is being made to breed a Call duck with a crest. There are crested Calls but none so far which have originated in this country, as yet, being bred to standard. Crested Calls do exist in this country which have been imported and are currently breeding.

In 1993 a programme was started to breed the first British Crested Call duck. This is not an undertaking for the faint hearted. It is a mammoth task involving the hatching of every egg laid and the extensive culling of resultant ducklings which have plain heads. As each and every duckling hatched is carrying the gene for crested, care must be taken that those ducklings that have the potential for being small are not culled.

The programme was started with a pair of Miniature Silver Crested. These were split and put to white Calls. The resultant daughters with some sort of crest were put back to the miniature crested drake and sons were put back to mother. The following year several pens were made up of the best and smallest second generation birds. Each successive year the best birds have been picked to be bred together. Progress has been made and there is a very small handful of birds that begin to resemble the Call duck but much work is needed before one will be able to see a true representation of a Crested Call.

A programme such as this should not be taken lightly for it involves considerable time, work and money. Ten years would not be an overestimate of the time needed to see real results and the whole enterprise can be wiped out by one visit by a passing predator. How often does one hear that someone has made great strides towards a given goal in selective breeding to have it completely wiped out. Not only predators, but the untimely death of a bird crucial to the breeding programme can set everything back by years. The work involved is intensive in the breeding season with the first cross frustrating as the disparity in size of the participants means that the incidence of infertile eggs is high, especially early in the season. One could say that the drake has to practise before he masters the art of successfully treading a duck dissimilar in size. Hatching the first cross is not too difficult, for one is, in effect, creating a hybrid and hybrid vigour would come into play.

Ensuing generations would prove to be more difficult as the incidence of crested offspring is akin to the incidence of hatching good Calls. If one considers the process through which the duckling goes to hatch, it becomes apparent that with an extra bump on its head this becomes more difficult. It is perhaps as well to warn potential breeders of crested birds that there are times when the duckling that hatches is a virtual monstrosity and arrives with the brain literally on the outside. These birds do not live very long and should be culled immediately. I have had it said to me by a well known breeder of crested birds that it is impossible to hatch them in an incubator.

Pampas Grass is also a good for protecting these magpie Calls of Evelyn van Vliet.

In a programme such as this it is advisable to keep records of the eggs set and where they came from. The resultant ducklings also should be traceable as it would be beneficial to know which pen of birds is producing the most viable youngsters. Here a programme of record keeping such as toe punching together with nicking the webs of the ducklings should be carried out and written records made to ensure that one knows which pen of birds is producing the best results. To breed a very good example of what you are aiming for and be unable to trace its origins would be frustrating to say the least.

When you have hatched every egg there then comes the decision as to whether every duckling is to be raised to maturity. From the moment the duckling emerges from the shell it is obvious whether it is to have a crest or not and, therefore, it is possible to cull the birds with plain heads.

Each bird carries a 50% gene bank for crested but one is breeding for size as well as crest so the resultant size of the duckling must also be taken into consideration as well as whether it has a crest or not. As each duckling carries the potential to breed crested whether it has a crest or not, each and every duckling should be viewed as a potential candidate for the breeding pen. A small crossbreed with strong Call attributes must not be discarded out of hand as it contains within it the ability to reproduce crested offspring if paired with the right partner. There is a school of thought in Holland, where Crested Calls are being produced, that one should never use a crested female, the reason being that the crest is formed by a fault in the skull which takes the form of a hole through which the brain protrudes. The crest is, therefore, the skin around that portion of the brain which exudes from the hole in the skull. Should the drake, when treading, catch hold of that particular place and seize the brain the duck will die. The gene responsible for producing crested birds is referred to as a lethal gene. As it is a flaw in the skull which is the means to protect the brain, one can quite see why it is referred to as a lethal gene. I have spoken to many people in this country on this subject and to date have not met anybody who has lost a female crested in this fashion. We do not as a rule in this country consider this factor in the breeding of crested ducks to be important nor, seemingly, have any reason to believe it.

It will be seen that to rear every duckling to adulthood involves time, space and money. In a venture such as this, unless one is sufficiently affluent, birds must be sold to enable the programme to continue. It is, of course, possible to sell the plain headed offspring in the local market or as pets but every bird sold is a candidate that might produce for its new owner the bird that you are endeavouring to breed. One does wonder whether there might already be Crested Calls awaiting discovery if the owner were to realise what he has. I have heard more than one tale of birds being rediscovered by an expert who just happened to be in the right place at the right time. Two instances come to mind. Firstly a red Muscovy was discovered in North Devon and secondly Red Billed Pintail. Birds that are thought to exist no longer are very often kept in farm yards or old collections of wildfowl.

I have no doubt at all that we shall, in the not too distant future, see the advent of the British Crested Call Duck. It will not be for the want of dedication if we do not.

Chapter 6 - Showing

'Oh no, I couldn't possibly show my birds. They aren't good enough,' is a familiar cry. Many people miss a great deal of fun and an enjoyable day out because they don't consider their birds to be good enough to show. What better way to spend a day than in the company of people who have the same interests and can teach much to the novice. Whatever class you enter, in any competition, there can only be one winner, and the rest, whether they be second, third or reserve are also rans. Personally I know if I did not enter my birds I would have no excuse to go to the show and probably wouldn't. Should I happen to win I have a bonus added to what is, for me, the culmination of a time in isolation during the breeding season. This hobby of ours tends to be a lonely one although much does depend on where one lives. Two years ago I bred a bird which was interesting, to say the least. Whilst I had various people here to buy birds, nobody who might appreciate her worth came for twelve months. She was finally seen in her second season when I took her to the various shows and then only selected ones where she would be under the minimum of stress, for she was precious and won many awards for me.

It is by taking our birds to a show that we can assess their worth. Many a bird looks to be a winner at home in its familiar pen. The minute it enters a show cage it can change. Gone is the little bird that scooted about the run showing off for your entertainment and in its place is an unhappy being which huddles into itself and skulks in the back of the cage. Fortunately this event is not seen often with Call ducks for they have an abundance of confidence and are more likely to stand there as if saying, 'Here I am. Look at me.' I had such a bird which was set to be a star. He stood in his cage and asked the world to look at him and he was stolen. There are exceptions to every rule and there was one winner on the show circuit who made it known that he was definitely bored with the whole affair and was hard put to stand up and show himself even when the judge's stick gave him the odd prod to do so. While it may be disappointing to find the birds you thought were quite good are not, it is instructive and steps can then be taken to improve the stock. Very often it is just a matter of buying in a fresh drake which, having come from promising stock, will give you a boost. How else can one really learn and progress if one's birds are not put to the test?

For the beginner, going to the first show can be a nerve wracking ordeal. I know for I have not forgotten the anxiety of my first shows and, having recently entered the dog showing world, realise afresh the trials and tribulations in attending that first show. Added to the nightmare that one's birds may be really hopeless is the fact one does not know what to do, where to go or how to find out. One of the biggest troubles is that you know no one and nobody talks to you. You wander around wondering what to do with yourself and whether it was worth all the trouble and thinking your bird looks terrible in the pen, a definite also ran. It did very well at the local poultry show but here at the waterfowl only show it wasn't even placed or, even worse, was beaten by one that it had already triumphed over. It must be remembered that usually at the local show it is a poultry judge who has had the dubious honour of judging what is for him or her a difficult task.

Chickens are their forte not waterfowl and they do the best they can. Do not despair. There are people there who are only too willing to talk to you once you have found the courage to approach them. We all started somewhere and most of us have not forgotten. Ask somebody who has organised the show. They are the ones who are dashing about with a white coat on. Ask them if they can point out somebody who will be willing to go over the finer points of your birds and help you. Once you have started talking you will find it difficult to stop. At the next show you will see familiar faces and, before you know it, shows will pass in a blur of conversation and you will wonder where the time went. I must admit that I have two 'minders', my husband and my son, who try to keep me in order. I have written an apology to one lady who asked me to look at her birds. While deep in conversation I became aware of my 'minders' standing beyond her glaring at me. Eventually my nerve broke and I terminated the conversation. We had been invited to partake of a drink and piece of cake to celebrate somebody's birthday and they were waiting to escort me to the venue. Not only to escort me but to repel any would be conversationalists on the way. The cake was delicious, the drink I refused, for, strangely, I have no taste for alcohol. The conversation was great for what other subject was there but 'ducks', Call ducks in particular.

There are two important points to remember when showing birds. The first is that if you do not enter your birds you are unlikely to go to the Show and secondly all your competitors may break down on the way!

One warning - having become hooked, showing can become an obsession - you will find yourself going to the shows come what may. The Hants and Berks Show in early January 1998 is a particular instance. The weather was appalling; heavy rain and gale force winds. The journey from the West Country was interesting to say the least and the journey home saw, when crossing Salisbury Plains, an articulated lorry facing our way on its side across the far side of the dual carriage way. There were few empty cages. On a previous occasion we set off from Cornwall with the threat of freezing fog hanging over us. When we entered the van the roof dripped with condensation. In Devon this condensation froze and thawed in Somerset. Salisbury Plain was a sight to behold with frost to the tops of the trees. To say it was beautiful is an understatement and to see it tinged in pink as the sun rose was a sight never to be forgotten. When we arrived at Whitchurch the boxes were frozen to the floor and the passengers' hair frozen to the side of the van. With our own vehicle off the road we were in a borrowed one which decided to die on us twice and was rejuvenated by judicious fiddling under the bonnet. No thought was given to turning back. On we went regardless and did arrive safely. Prolonged fiddling while at the show ensured that there was only one occasion homewards when the engine decided it might die again.

It is one of the easiest things imaginable to prepare your Calls for the show cage. When I send my entry in to the Show Secretary I usually mark my schedule as a copy for myself and put this in a safe place because not all shows send out a list of the pen numbers before a show. I usually manage to find something to put in a cage which will not disgrace me and I will go so far as to say that having entered a bird one owes it to the judge to fill the cage if at all possible. If one is unable to go to a show it is one thing but, finding the bird entered unfit, one should put in a substitute if possible. People who give up their time to judge do so for little recompense, doing it because they have some expertise in the breed and in the hope that by doing so they will further its future.

With the list between my teeth I proceed to catch the birds, I proceed to the duck runs picking up the fisherman's landing net on the way. I half fill the bath with water and put a house brick over the plug because one of my drakes has learnt how to pull it out. You will discover if you have overfilled the bath as tidal waves will erupt over the edge and I advise you to lower the level of the water quickly. If you have a shower unit this is equally good, if not better, for you can pull the curtain around the birds and enclose the spray. Put the plug in the bath, turn the shower unit on, add the ducks and walk away. Do remember to return shortly. One lady I know put the plug in, turned on the shower, added several Muscovies and had visitors. At a later stage she remembered the ducks. One was crossing the landing to meet her, one was sitting on the wash hand basin, one was roosting on the edge of the bath and the water was about to overflow!

If you do not have constant clean water you may need to improvise by allowing your ducks the run of the bathroom to clean themselves before exhibiting them.

With the birds splashing happily away getting rid of any mud on feet and beaks your next task is to cover an area of floor with a thick layer of newspaper and top this with towels. This is to place the birds on to drip dry and to preen themselves. It is necessary to let them dry for once in the box, if they are wet, shavings do tend to stick to them.

After about half an hour or so the birds will have had a wonderful time and be ready for the next stage. I have not discovered a foolproof way of catching the birds without getting wet but would suggest you con somebody else into doing it (in my case husband or son). You don waterproof clothing, switch off the light and proceed with caution. Birds new to this experience are easiest to catch. The old hands dive around under water enthusiastically.

One thoroughly professional tip is to empty the bath immediately after the birds have been removed. Should you have visitors and you haven't done this they will look askance at you. It is not everybody who will believe you have had ducks on the bath in the first place. It is handy also to have a separate loo as I have had my sister-in-law's husband flee the bathroom in disarray having been caught in the spray from a tidal wave. My husband will tell you it is the only time of the year our bathroom is completely clean for he has to wipe the ceiling off as well as the walls and floor. While I do not recommend arthritis in the shoulders it does come in handy sometimes especially when the bathroom ceiling needs drying off!

Off the water and onto dry land again the birds become busy putting feathers in order and generally getting themselves ready. When you can see that they are dry, then is the time to box them up. Once boxed you can either put the birds in the car ready for the morning or stack them up in a safe place overnight. At the show the next day, before you put your bird in the correct cage, a smear of Vaseline on the bill or a wipe over with a tissue impregnated with baby oil will give it a professional look. Not too much of either for the little darling will root around in the shavings looking for food and get itself covered, thus spoiling the effect you have striven to create. I find it a good idea to mark each box with the colour, class number and pen number, if you have it, so that when you arrive at the show the next morning things are easy. There is nothing more panic making than to be late through no fault of your own and to be trying to decide which bird you were going to put in what class. If a friend offers to help you that can save time. Beware though, for I once put a friend's ducks in the drake class and her drakes in the duck class. The judge came up to me afterwards and informed me what 'some idiot' had done and was rather taken aback when I replied, 'Yes it was me.' Needless to say, as soon as my friend arrived in the afternoon I rushed to her and confessed before somebody else told her.

Food and water should not be placed in the cage before judging. One exception would be if you have travelled all day to a show and have caged the birds the night before. It is a good idea to arrive at the show the next morning early to remove the drinker and to add fresh shavings if they have made the pen very wet. Ducks can make an extraordinary amount of mess with one small container of water and also if your drinkers are distinctive it could be construed as telling the judge which birds are yours, as would putting food in a particular place.

It must be up to the individual to decide whether it is ethical to enter birds under a judge who is a personal friend and who might or might not be familiar with their birds. I have never had any qualms about entering under any one judge. Whilst I like to win, if my bird is good enough, it is not as important as going to the show and meeting the people.

Whoever the judge is, you are asking him for his opinion of your bird. The entry that wins the class is the result of his opinion. Whether you agree with him or not is not the issue for he has given you his opinion. You may think you deserved to win, your friends may also, but if the judge is not of the same opinion so be it.

We are moving into a new age with the Calls when new colours are appearing almost yearly. Life with colours is becoming difficult and very often a bird is put into a class with all good intentions and then one finds it is not what one thought it was. I have to say I consider, if this is the case, the bird should be transferred rather than disqualified, for with all these new colours the beginner is at a severe disadvantage and when enumerating the various colours to a newcomer one realises just how confusing it all is. I will add that not only does the beginner need to be told which colour is which, I myself not so very long ago asked to have Silver explained to me.

The mark of an outstanding bird must be when more than one judge puts it first. If your bird has won consistently throughout a season under different judges it is fair to say you are then allowed to consider you have got it right. If you can do it for more than one season with the same bird you are doing well, for hot on your heels will be that young duck just panting on the starting line to knock you off your perch. Then you have to go back to the drawing board and produce the next one and that is the difficult part. Show winners do not crop up every year, they appear occasionally. Thank goodness is what I say, for life would be boring otherwise. In each and every class you enter there can be only one winner. To test your bird to its limit a big waterfowl show is the answer with plenty of competition. Winning in a class of 2 is fine, you have beaten something, winning in a class of 30 or 40 has to be the ultimate. Then you know your duck is good. I was once rung up by a lady who wanted to sell her birds. 'They won at Wadebridge,' I was told. 'Yes I know they did,' I thought, 'they were the only ones there!'

Sportsmanship is needed in the world of showing waterfowl as it is in any competitive field. Hearing somebody moaning at a show about a judge one day I was then asked why I didn't judge. 'Ha,' I laughed, 'then you would be moaning about me.' I must confess to being surprised once or twice by a judge's decision and to knowing, since I have been doing it for so long, whether we are in with a chance or not. Very often I find I was mistaken but on one occasion I was heard to offer the opinion that the judge must have left her glasses at home for when my best duck came fourth, my second best duck came second and my drake won, a thing he didn't usually do. It was not an unreasonable conclusion! It is all part of the fun. Judge's opinion is final.

Assessing Calls

It takes time and experience to become familiar with what one is looking for in a good Call. To consider only the head is all too easy when we should be looking at the whole bird. It is the head that draws the eye but care should be taken to include the rest of the bird in your assessment. Size is important also but to my mind there is nothing wrong with a slightly bigger bird if it has all the attributes of a good Call. Reading the standard helps but we all interpret it in a different way. What appeals to one does not appeal to another but in each case may depict the standard. Until recently I had never analysed what constituted a good Call I just knew that a particular bird took my eye and had the 'look' that I desired.

It is a great pity that we cannot keep the majority of our annual offspring for more than twelve months after they have been hatched for they do improve tremendously. Viewing a young man's current offering I recommended that he discard a particular duck. The following year while once again in the process of giving my opinion, I suddenly espied a particular bird and was most enthusiastic. 'You told me to neck her last year,' was the response I received. I promptly dissolved into laughter - we all make mistakes!

A nice head of a Silver duck showing cream in cheek.

Once you have your eye in it is possible to study a brood of ducklings and pick out one or two good ones. Size will be the unknown factor for some bigger ducks lay small eggs and size of duckling does not always denote size of the adult bird. As the ducklings grow they change dramatically and you will view them with despair for they will all look, at one stage, to be a load of rubbish. This is known within the hobby as 'the teenage stage'. I am firmly of the opinion that the beak grows to its full size long before the body and this is why that lovely duckling disappears. Once the ducklings have reached full size they will change and that 'little gem' will reappear. Drakes tend to be elusive for it is not until they are fully coloured that they show their full potential although if they are of excellent type you will be aware of it.

Grey female of Tony Penny's which has an excellent shaped head.

Sadly, downfaced birds will suddenly get a higher head and the drakes will improve out of all recognition when they are in full colour. The forehead of a bird which is 'downfaced' slopes straight up from the top of the beak, making the head flat instead of round. In some birds this is not the end of the world and they do improve and those birds that do not, if they have a good body, can be included in a breeding pen with a bird that has a particularly good head. Some of the offspring will show an improvement and with careful selection over a number of years birds with good heads and bodies will evolve. It will take a number of years for one cannot in all honesty expect to achieve perfection at any time and certainly not in a short time.

Having bred, after 17 years, a delightful Blue Fawn drake only to have him stolen from the back lawn, I was fortunate in that I still had the stock birds from which he was produced. As not only he but his mother, brother and two sisters were stolen I should have been sunk without a trace had I been depending solely on them. To have a phone call from a person, who has subsequently become a close friend, offering me a drake of my breeding was very touching and gratifying. To be able to give my heartfelt thanks and say I still had the stock was reassuring.

Very often it is the smallest of a brood which is the best bird and the show quality bird. By this I do not mean a runt. The smallest of the brood would be referred to as the runt but it is the runt that grows up that should be retained. A true runt is no good to man nor beast and certainly has no place in the breeding pen for the true runt does not breed. What use is a duck that does not lay and, therefore, is unable to reproduce herself? She is taking up valuable space and is being fed for no reason. Drakes that are runts, while they may be fertile, are unable to tread successfully. I am continually talking to people who have very poor expectations of the number of eggs their birds will lay. On some occasions this is due to a short season but in many instances it is because birds have been continually retained from birds that are poor layers. A duck that lays few eggs produces female offspring that lay few eggs. It is tempting to continue if the offspring are good but it is a suicidal path.

The runt, being so small, lays few viable eggs. A duck with good type which is bigger lays more eggs. If in doing so she also produces that smaller bird of show standard she is the one for you. I must confess that it is the breeding of the show bird that fascinates me most and if I can keep in my breeding pens birds which win as well as produce good show specimens and lay well I am content. There is nothing like a sensible sized bird that has good type. I am often asked if I have any eggs for sale. The answer is always in the negative. I never have eggs surplus to requirements once fertility has arrived. I could never part with a single egg for I may be parting with the egg that contains the 'perfect' bird. The eggs sold may be infertile and while it has been said to me that one takes one's chance when buying eggs, it is not everybody's view. Eggs that are fertile can be mishandled and the blame put on the vendor. Just what amount would one charge for them? Having a broody hen and nothing to put under her is not a good enough reason for me to part with my precious eggs and somehow or other I get the feeling that I am being asked for something for relatively nothing.

Blue Fawn drake which is only 15 weeks old showing excellent domed head with the full colour to come. Bred by Tony Penny.

'I only want them for pets' is another suspicious statement for me. No doubt there are some people who genuinely want them for pets, but others I fear are hoping for birds from good stock at small cost, whereby, if they are lucky, they can breed good birds. Am I being unfair? Perhaps in some cases but in others definitely not. Show me real endeavour and enthusiasm and I will help in any way I can.

Selling Stock

One of the most frustrating aspects of selling birds is 'orders'. People will enquire after a particular colour or will come, view your collection and order birds for collection or delivery when you have them available. While they are quite genuine at the time of placing the order it will be found in many instances that when you contact them to say their birds are ready they will either have changed their mind or acquired birds elsewhere. This can be very annoying, especially if you have gone to some trouble to produce the birds or even to arrange how you are going to unite the birds with their future owners. Over the years I have developed the policy that I suggest to the interested parties that they contact me again at a future date, which I give them, when I shall know if I have the birds available and when they can collect them. Those who are really interested do so and I will go to no end of trouble to satisfy their requirements. For the genuine customer there is no difficulty in doing so.

There can be no better way of buying birds than direct from the breeder, for not only can you view the bird in its normal environment but you can assess whether it is fit and well and get a better idea of how it behaves. A bird in a cage at an auction cannot be seen to its best advantage and should you discover it is lame or even blind in one eye (for it will stand with its good eye towards you in the cage) having bought it 'as seen' there is no come back. The breeder can give you the history of the bird, how it was bred, some idea of its ancestry and whether you are likely to get any surprises when you breed with it. Birds that have been bred by chance may be one colour themselves but behind them are several other colours. This is rather exciting as you will never know what to expect from a clutch of eggs but disheartening if your aim is to breed a certain colour. Most breeders will attempt to put things right if you lose a bird from no fault of yours but I do ask to see the carcass. You may be honest but others are not. There must be a time limit and I stipulate one week. It takes an experienced breeder to notice that a bird is ailing for waterfowl in general show very few signs of illness. Loss of condition is not noticeable until the bird is failing. Unless the bird is handled, and few of us are picking up every bird all of the time, quite often signs of illness are not apparent until it is too late. When they are caught, significant loss of condition will be evident in a light, skinny body, in which case that particular bird should not be sold. However, birds can live quite happily with a latent disease which is only triggered when a period of stress is experienced. Being caught, boxed, transported and put down in a strange environment is stress. Being caught, boxed, transported, caged to be viewed at very close quarters, subjected to noise, heat or cold and transported again to be put out in a strange environment is a significant stress. If there is a question mark over the health of any bird it is inadvisable to subject it to any stress at all until you are sure in your own mind that it is fully fit.

An advert in the local paper can bring useful results although there will be some time wasting. Having become totally fed up with people phoning in answer to my various advertisements, asking the price and then telling me they would have to speak to husband, mother, father, etc. and never heard from again, the next advert I placed stated the price of every type of bird offered for sale. I thought I had covered all angles and only genuine enquiries would be received. I was mistaken for I was asked if I had any eggs for sale and then had my price per bird mistaken for price per pair. Another well known ploy is for people to say they will have the birds and will be in touch when they are in the area. They may come into your area to visit relations or upon business matters. It is as well if you ask them when this is likely to be for you may find yourself feeding these particular birds for weeks or even months before they are collected.

It is extremely annoying to have your price questioned and there are various ploys to make it seem as though you were not clear when you gave the price, if indeed you were asked for one. Nowadays when I give a price I write it down immediately. I then have a record and when the bird or birds are being collected I can, should I be in any doubt, check. It is sensible to decide what you are going to charge for your birds and stick to it. When people buy birds by auction they do, on occasions, buy them cheaply and should there be someone in your area who habitually reduces surplus substandard stock through the local market he will be expecting you to sell him a bird at the same price. When I am faced with shocked amazement over my price I politely inform the caller that he or she has dialled the wrong number. One should have confidence in one's birds. That does not mean that if I am faced with a youngster starting out in Calls that I charge a high price. It is up to all of us to encourage the young people who wish to start out in this hobby of ours. However I do practise some degree of caution for, not so very long ago, I sold a pair of very nice birds at a reduced price to a young man and discovered that he had purchased a single drake for twice the price of my pair!

There are a few times when I refuse to sell my birds to a particular person for the grapevine does tend to be infallible and one does hear, occasionally, that so and so keeps his or her birds in appalling conditions or one is asked time and again for birds by the same person because the fox has once again eaten them. It is quite possible to ignore these warnings but personally I do try to the best of my ability to see that the birds I have taken time and trouble over do not meet an unnecessary end or become subjected to miserable conditions.

Word of mouth, if you consistently provide good birds, will eventually take over and it will be found unnecessary to advertise at all. The building up of a reputation, over a period of time, having established your reliability, honesty, fairness and knowledge, has no substitute. We all make mistakes and fate plays its part at times. Rather than complain to the world at large, tell the breeder of your birds what has gone wrong and see if he or she can help. It is very damaging and distressing to be vilified behind your back, being given no chance to defend yourself. Remember, because you have bought birds from a successful flock you will not necessarily have success in the first season nor, come to that, the next.

Judging of Ducks by Ian Kay

The judging technique for all breeds of small duck is very similar to that for any other breed. Each judge may have his own favoured procedure which in certain instances may not receive the full approval of all the exhibitors present. However, if he eventually places birds in the correct order then all will be forgiven.

To commence, I would like to explain a few points from past decades. Firstly, for many years the number of Waterfowl exhibited at many of the shows did not warrant the engagement of a specialist judge, consequently, the judging of a few duck classes was quickly added to a poultry judge who did not have a full quota of birds to judge. Quite frequently this was to his utter surprise and once the complications and implications had dawned on him, it was to his total dismay.

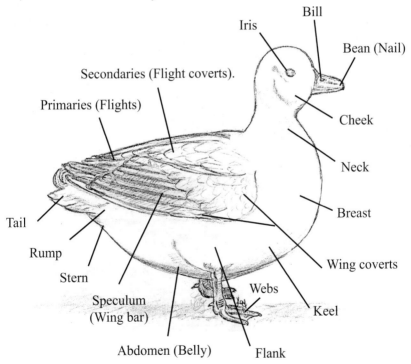

Labelled parts of a duck.

It would not be an understatement to say that, in the past, many of the show societies did not take Waterfowl seriously, indeed, some of them did not include classes for them in their schedule. In many instances these quick judging arrangements did not cause too many problems owing to the low number of entries and the fact that many of the birds belonged to one exhibitor.

The very successful promoting of domestic waterfowl by the British Waterfowl Association achieved their objective in increasing the status of the once neglected duck. They were increasing in popularity with additional classes being included in many of the show schedules.

The period around 1980 witnessed the 'Call duck explosion' which brought with it a large number of new and enthusiastic duck breeders. This was great for the fancy, but there was still a shortage of qualified judges. Entries at the shows were increasing, especially in the Bantam ducks. However, circulation of an approved standard for the small breeds of duck was rather limited and consequently some of the judges who were not too sure of their knowledge in these more recently popular breeds sought advice from whatever source they thought could supply them with a brief summary of the birds they were shortly to judge.

Unfortunately, when a judge has a limited amount of knowledge in a breed he tends to use a particular feature of the bird as the ultimate in perfection rather than assess an overall picture of each exhibit. This situation can arise in other species, the wing markings on Rhode Island Red Fowl and the hackle markings in Light Sussex are prime examples of over emphasising a particular feature.

In Call ducks it is the head which has dominated, especially in the length of beak. This is probably the result of an unsure judge having a consultation with a so called 'expert'. In his attempt to obtain some quick information on the new breed which he is soon to judge, the head has been the main topic for discussion. Unfortunately, the hastily acquired mentor has failed to mention the fact that even though the head receives 20 points in the standard, it still leaves a further 80 points to be assessed in the remaining parts of the bird!

There is a danger of this interpretation of the breed being continued in future years. The strength of Call duck fanciers in the country at the present time allows a person who is conversant with the breed to be appointed to judge. The show societies are continually expanding their classification and there is also the addition of specialist Waterfowl only shows, so hopefully the situation will be corrected.

However, looking into my crystal ball, I can see a situation developing where we have an adequate supply of Call experts who will be asked to judge the other 20 breeds of Duck. So I do ask that anyone wishing to become a judge spends time increasing his or her knowledge and appreciation of the other breeds, rather than be just a specialist. Speaking from personal experience in promoting shows, I can assure all readers that the appointment of judges is not a simple task, especially when most societies are now on a tight financial budget.

In the continuing part of this chapter, I will offer some advice which should prove helpful to newcomers contemplating becoming 'The Waver of a Magic Wand'.

A German bred Mallard drake

The accepted technique for judging Waterfowl has for many decades differed from the one used to assess Poultry and Bantams, the main difference being in the removing of exhibits from their show pen. In poultry there can be many hidden faults which require a closer inspection by the judge. This should be carried out after all the birds in the class have been carefully assessed and recorded from outside their pens.

In Waterfowl many of these potential faults do not come into a judge's consideration, examples being wing markings on the flight and secondary feathers, as in Rhode Island Red and Sussex fowl, also the attention paid to the colouring of the birds' lower feathering, which is commonly called 'undercolour'. Rhode Island Reds are again an example, where their top colour should extend right down to the skin. Black Wyandottes should carry their colour to the feather roots and not carry a white disfiguration. In most breeds of Ducks any inspection of the undercolour is virtually non existent as is inspection of the flight feathers.

Crooked breasts are very rare in Waterfowl, whilst crooked tails and roach backs can easily be detected from outside the pen. The same applies to 'bow leg', 'knock knees', 'twisted beaks' and 'wry necks'. Consequently, much of the judging in Waterfowl has been completed without removing the birds from their show pen.

There is a tendency for Ducks to be more nervous than Poultry and this method of judging reduces the risk of damage to either the bird or its feathers. There will always be the occasion where a Rouen duck requires a closer inspection to ascertain the depth of her lacing or perhaps to check the outer wing flights in a Blue Swedish. Self black ducks require a check for white under their throat, but most of the old fashioned breeds of duck could be well assessed from outside the pen and any closer inspection left until the birds had been well studied whilst standing in their natural position. Shape and general outline, including the head, account for a major part of the bird in many of the Duck breeds, Aylesburys and Indian Runners being prime examples.

In the judging of Bantam and Call ducks during the last few years of the twentieth century the procedure of removing birds from their show pens is gradually increasing. In most instances these small ducks are quieter in temperament and certainly much easier to handle, especially as many of the birds shown are their owner's 'pet' and well used to being caressed and 'molly-coddled'.

Therefore there is a strong case for many more of these birds being judged in the hand, but, as with poultry, only after a careful assessment when they are standing in their natural position. Once removed from its pen a bird of nervous disposition can take a long time to settle back into a relaxed posture and thus show its correct shape. Another point in favour of hand inspection is that with the Calls being so much smaller than, say, an Aylesbury, their head features are less obvious from outside the pen, especially as their pens are smaller and in some cases not open topped when they are displayed several tiers high.

When removing the birds from their pens do so with great care. Remember that they are not your birds they are someone else's pride and joy and you are only being privileged to inspect them for the day, after which the owner wishes to have them returned home in 100% condition.

It is my belief that a judge should have the patience to try and pursuade every exhibit to show itself to its highest potential. This may take a little extra time but very often a bird which is not fully 'pen trained' and therefore nervous, belongs to a person who is new to showing. These people warrant all the help possible. There have been many instances where a keen new enthusiast has been lost forever due to some unfortunate incident at his/her first few shows. Birds vary in temperament, as do their owners, but in general they require a lot of 'pen training' before they feel fully relaxed and therefore look at their best. Much of this training should be done at home. When a breeder has selected some of the best specimens from his current year's flock of youngsters, it is usual to bring them into the penning room where they are given a few hours of life in a show pen. They can then be returned to their run and the procedure repeated for several days, during which time their time in a show pen is increased.

Some breeders pen them in singles but I find that they settle better if given a companion to share their pen with. You will find that some birds are natural show offs and immediately display themselves, very often these are the birds which go on to win major awards. They are also excellent for breeding purposes where much of their self assurance can be transmitted to their progeny. The ones which do not readily adapt to show pens require much patience with a little help from feeding them tit-bits at the pen front and regular handling.

Another point which they will have to be taught is that the insertion of a 'judging stick' through the pen front means stand to attention, and be on your best behaviour; you are now being assessed. It is the lack of basic training which prompted me to suggest that, as a judge, you attempt to pursuade a shy bird to show itself rather than walk swiftly past without considering that maybe, with a little coaxing, there is some potential in the bird. Judges vary in their choice of stick which is used to gently move the bird into a more favourable or viewable position. I myself favour a longish stick, especially for large birds. This enables me to stand well back whilst assessing the bird in question and still be able to move it slightly, should I so wish, a manoeuvre which is completed without moving close to the pen and possibly disturbing the bird's natural stance.

I also believe that standing well away from the pen allows the bird more freedom to express itself. Exhibitors will find that it can take several shows before a bird is fully capable of displaying itself to its full potential. Training a bird at home is one thing, but being placed in a hall with dozens of strange people rushing around is a whole new world, especially after the stress of just being introduced to a 'duck hut on wheels', which flew down the motorway at 80 m.p.h., because the owner was late getting out of bed. It is very beneficial to arrive at the show early and give your stock time to settle from their journey especially with the ones who suffer from car sickness. A little food and a drink of water can often help to settle them down in their showpen.

To be a good judge I believe that it is helpful to have the ability to assess the overall strengths and weaknesses of a bird without being greatly influenced by one particular feature of its standard. It is also very easy to adopt a negative approach whereby simple little faults are used as virtual disqualifications. In most of the breeds the standard lists the points which are disqualifications. Usually these are structural deformities and are quite rightly recommended to be immediately condemned from the show pen. Such birds should never have been reared never mind shown. Most of these deformities are hereditary and any sign of encouragement to exhibit such birds would be detrimental to their breed.

The points which I have in mind which can be over-emphasised are where a small but easily noticeable fault is downgraded to a far greater degree than the allocation of points in that bird's standard has indicated. Examples of this would be a few spots of black in the bill of an adult white Call or Indian Runner duck, or perhaps being too severe on white feathers around the eye of old drakes and ducks on Black East Indians.

In a general way let your brain work as a computer to calculate an overall assessment of the bird's good features whilst at the same time subtracting points for its bad ones.

Good head.

Narrow head.

Square head.

Wedge head with flat crown

Head too narrow. Pinched vertically.

Good round head.

Flat head and scooped bill.

*No rise to dome and too long
a bill in proportion to head.*

This possibly controversial statement is written on purpose to lead me directly onto the different methods of judging or assessing that are conducted in the various countries of the world. Basically there are two types of judging; firstly the one which is used at almost every show in the British Isles where the best few birds are simply allocated awards in descending order of merit from first to fourth, or at some of the larger shows down to seventh.

This system apparently suits the British exhibitors as most of the attempts at altering the system have been received with luke warm participation, especially amongst the well established breeders.

The alternative procedure is for each exhibit to be fully assessed against the standard of perfection, with the results then being displayed on their pen fronts. This system is used in many countries. The final conclusion varies from country to country but the principal of each bird having an assessment remains the same.

This type of judging I believe is very beneficial to newcomers as it conveys to them the good and bad features in their stock without having to locate the judge and request a personal hearing of his opinion on their birds. It can however reduce the competitive spirit which is apparently very appealing to the British fancier who obtains great pleasure from a friendly rivalry with fellow exhibitors, many of whom are also good friends. Winning a red ticket is the all important feature of the show day.

In some of the other countries this is still possible even when individual bird assessment has taken place. There are other instances when several birds accumulate the same score and are then awarded equal first prize.

Judging to our system requires a smaller number of judges which can be beneficial to the show organisers' finances. It also takes less office administration. There are many people who believe that to judge by the British system requires less skill and knowledge than the continental one. The judge is certainly exempt from having to record any written explanations for his awards, but he should still remain in the hall after judging is completed and thus be available to verbally answer any queries.

This system works well for the smaller shows and especially at the Agricultural Shows where the general public are anxious to see the awards as quickly as possible. In days gone by many societies expected a judge to be able to adjudicate on between 60 and 100 birds per hour. In Europe they recommend no more than 80 animals per day. Personally, I favour some form of written critique at the major shows, especially the main club show where many new breeders are anxiously competing against the long established exhibitors. An assessment card offers them a guideline as to their birds potential even though it might not be good enough to finish in the top few birds in the class. This is especially relevant when there are large classes with many good birds left cardless due to the strength of opposition.

I find that when judging to the two different systems you need to adopt a slightly different approach and technique. If your terms of engagement are simply to select the best four birds in each class then your task should be relatively easy providing that the general quality of birds present is near to standard. If there are a lot of poor specimens then your task becomes much harder, especially when you know that as soon as the cards go on the pens, people will be saying, 'Look at that bad beggar he has just given first prize.' Providing that the birds present are the usual mixture of qualities when you take your first walk along the pens, there are usually some birds with obvious faults which immediately record in your mind as reducing them to 'also rans'; conversely there will be birds which look full of promise and you wiil be eager to give them a closer inspection. I like to detect what appears to be the best bird from outside the pen, inspect it, and if it justifies its early possibilities, I return it to its pen and then start at the beginning of the class to try and find some better birds. Before removing any birds from their pens I make a note of all the ones which are showing good shape and stance, knowing that after removal from the pen this may be temporarily lost.

An often debated point now arises. Do you spend time inspecting birds which you know full well will not finish in the top flight, never mind the top four? There are many owners who state that they have paid an entry fee to have a judge's assessment. This would be correct if shown under the alternative system, but with 'comparative judging' it is only the best birds which figure in a judge's final selection so what is the reason for him recording faults which cannot be displayed on the pen? If an exhibitor comes to me after judging enquiring about his exhibit then I am more than willing to spend time with him or her discussing both the good and bad features of the bird in question, and it is on this side of the debate that I cast my vote.

When making the final selections, I like to have in my mind definite reasons for the decisions I have arrived at. If you do not have a good memory it is sound practice to make a few quick notes in your judging book. The question of a steward to assist a judge is often discussed. I do not appreciate one unless it is a member of the family or close friend who knows how I operate. They keep quiet and simply do the book work. If it is someone you do not know you feel obliged to carry on some form of conversation which detracts my brain from the job in hand. This reduces efficiency and slows down the whole procedure.

On occasions it has been said to me that a certain person would like to accompany me and learn about some of the breeds with which he is not fully conversant. I have always replied that if people wish to go round with me after judging then I would be only too pleased to help them, but during judging I prefer to be fully involved with trying to place the birds in the correct order of merit. Outside my family where son Dean and daughter Ulanda have helped me since being five years old, with John and Stuart helping in their later years, there are two people whom I would like to thank for being patient book keepers at many different shows. They are Ernie Thorpe and Daphnie Hope who must have spent many boring hours trailing after me!

One point for a judge to take into consideration is the amount to which he is influenced by show preparation. This mainly applies to pure white coloured birds. In poultry it is overwhelmingly accepted that all white birds should be thoroughly washed prior to exhibition. The same procedure does not apply to waterfowl where many breeders show their stock naturally washed in their habitat. However, not everyone has running water and at certain times of the year artificial ponds can become dirty in their surrounding areas.

Consequently, it has become almost necessary for exhibitors to shampoo their birds prior to showing them. Many people are against this practice, believing that the washing of a duck in either liquid soap or hair shampoo destroys the natural oils in its plumage. This may be correct, but, as with poultry, many bantam ducks are increasingly being kept in a limited space and controlled environment where this problem, if it occurs, is not so evident. Birds which are shown in a pure white plumage are certainly eye catching to a judge and really, providing that no dying or artificial colouring has been added to their feathers, no rules have been broken.

Shallow long body. Legs too far back.

Shallow stern.

Off balance, tipping back.

Off balance, tipping forward.

Breast too shallow.

Drooping stern.

99

It is normal procedure to apply a smear of baby oil to both the legs and beak in all types of waterfowl, which again adds a touch of showmanship to the birds. This attention to detail by the exhibitor certainly pays dividends and deserves to receive recognition, but a judge must be careful not to be over influenced by presentation at the expense of shape, style and markings etc.

A point which I am often asked to comment on is the question of friends showing birds under you when you are judging. I believe that where there are two people working in a partnership, or in close relationship with their breeding programme then it is not acceptable, nor is it sensible. Any victory would be treated sceptically by most of the other exhibitors. However, I like to believe that I have many friends, and the only way to judge the birds is to place them in the correct order of merit and wait until after judging to find out which of your friends have been the winners.

The most important point is, as I said earlier, be sure that you have at your finger tips the reasons behind your adjudication.

Being a judge does not appeal to everyone, possibly due to each person's different personality and nature. I thoroughly enjoy the occupation and have done so for over 50 years. My suggestion to anyone being invited to judge for the first time, is accept the challenge, simply go there and enjoy yourself. You are only being asked to offer your opinion on the exhibits placed before you. A vital point to bear in mind is that the task is only the same as you will have done on many occasions at home, that is to select from your batch of youngsters the ones which are most likely to be the winners.

A final point to bear in mind is that should everyone not agree with your placings, you can't be hanged for it!

The judging of any species is conducted by comparing the exhibit against the standard of perfection for that breed. These standards are usually defined by each individual breed club and then passed on to the British Waterfowl Association or the Poultry Club for ratification. In the case of bantam ducks, the British standards are held jointly by the B.W.A. and the P.C.

In America there are two organisations which issue standards. They are the American Poultry Association (APA) and American Bantam Association (ABA)

In some cases they vary slightly and Call ducks are one breed which differs. The A.B.A. states 70 points for shape and 30 points for colour (74/26 points in the White), whilst the A.P.A. allocates 64 points for shape and 36 points for colour (72/28 for the White). Both of them are consistent in allowing fewer points for a self coloured bird as against a coloured one.

This is a feature which could well be adopted in this country and may well be altered in the future. Until recently the only colours officially approved for Calls were White, Mallard, (Fawn or Grey), Blue Fawn, Pied and Silver.

The points allocated for these birds were Type 30, Size 20, colour 30, Head, including neck and bill, 15, legs and feet 5, with condition accounting for the remaining 10 points. Interestingly, the breed was not named the Call Duck, but the Decoy, which was the name used in the nineteenth century.

The main serious faults were listed as:- thin boat shaped bodies, thin bills and flat headed skulls. A copy of the exact standard including colourings can be obtained from either the P.C. or the B.W.A.

In very recent years a whole series of new coloured Call ducks have been appearing in this country and the newly formed British Call Duck Society has now issued a suggested guideline as to their correct colouring. I believe that it will prove very useful to many new exhibitors who are just commencing breeding these very attractive colour variations and we therefore reproduce their suggestions in full as follows.

Give Call ducks a bowl of clean water and they are happy as these blue fawns are.

Suggested standards for non standardised colours from The British Call Duck Club.

The Dark Silver

Drake's plumage: Head as light silver. Breast as light silver but more solid claret with less white fringing. Back dark grey with black frosting shading to black with beetle green sheen on rump. Some light claret feathers extending along flanks, each feather edged with white. Scapulars dark grey with brown outer edge, smaller scapulars with claret outer edge. Grey frosting on belly. Wing flights grey with grey frosting on primaries and secondaries. Speculum blue with black then white band on secondaries. Bands missing from coverts of secondaries. Tertiaries light brown with heavy silver grey frosting. Tail central feathers darker, each feather having grey centre and pale edging. Rump under cushion black with green sheen. Bill green with black bean. Eyes brown.

Duck's plumage: Head and back of neck buff with darker brown graining. Light buff throat, faint light buff eye stripes. Breast, flanks and back feathers, rich buff with narrow pencilling of darker brown on each feather. Under body cream with dark brown flecking. Wing coverts light brown with cream edging, speculum and borders as drake. Tertiaries and primaries as coverts, scapulars as flanks and back. Tail upper and under coverts brown with cream edging. Bill dark orange with brown saddle. Eyes brown.

The Penny Black

Drake's and duck's plumage: Apart from some green lustre on the heads of drakes, both sexes to be a matt black all over. The less lustre the better. Legs and feet to be as black as possible but a very dark tan is acceptable at this stage. Eyes and bill should be as black as possible in both sexes.

Minor faults: Russet mottling in breast feathers and under tail coverts. Dark chestnut or brown main flight and tail feathers. White feathers in either sex would be more of a fault as would green lustre on females.

The Glossy Black

To have all Call duck type but to emulate the Black East Indian in colour of plumage which would be a very lustrous, intense, beetle green black. Brown or white feathers in either sex are undesirable. Bill, eyes, legs and feet to be as black as possible.

The Dark Apricot Silver

Drake's plumage: Head silvery grey with white collar completely encircling neck. Breast as light apricot silver but a more solid mulberry with less white fringing. Back; light silvery grey frosting shading to darker grey on rump and under tail coverts. Flanks are a dark mulberry along the upper with light grey frosting on lower and belly. Wing flights of grey with frosted primaries and secondaries, speculum dark grey with white borders, tertiaries grey with mulberry edging. Scapulars mulberry and grey, wing coverts mulberry edged with grey. Tail outer feathers white, central feathers light silver grey. Bill light green with dark bean. Eyes brown.

Duck's plumage: Head and back of neck apricot with dark grey graining, apricot eye stripes and cream throat. Breast, flanks and back apricot with broad pencilling of dark grey on each feather. Underbody light beige with grey flecking. Wing primaries and secondaries grey and apricot with grey coverts having beige edging, speculum and borders as drake, tertiaries and scapulars grey and apricot. Tail upper and under coverts, outer feathers light beige with dark brown stippling gradually darkening towards centre. Bill dark orange with brown saddle. Eyes brown.

Defects: White collar not completely encircling neck on drake.

The Light Apricot Silver

Drake's plumage: Head silver grey with white collar completely encircling neck. Breast mulberry, each feather laced with white, mulberry split by more white on lower breast. Upper flanks light mulberry feathers with white edging, lower flanks and belly white. Back white with light grey frosting shading to darker grey feathers edged with white on rump. Wing flights white, speculum light grey with white band on tip of secondaries, tertiaries mulberry edged with white. Wing coverts white. Tail white outer feathers, grey central and under tail. Bill light green with dark bean. Eyes brown.

Duck's plumage : Head and upper neck light apricot, cream flecking on crown, no eye stripes. Body white with apricot mottling on shoulders and breast. Light apricot mottling on lower back preferred. Wing flights white, speculum light grey with white band on tip of secondaries as drake, tertiaries white blending to apricot with grey on edges, wing coverts white edged with apricot. Tail white with light apricot mottling on upper tail coverts. Bill light orange. Eyes brown. Defects: White collar not completely encircling neck on drake. Dark graining on head of duck.

The Dark Blue Silver

Drake's plumage: Head charcoal-blue with white collar encircling neck. Breast claret, each feather laced with white, claret split with more white on lower breast. Back light grey with darker grey frosting shading to charcoal-blue on rump. Light claret feathers edged with white along the upper flanks, light grey frosting on lower flanks and belly. Wing flights grey, speculum charcoal blue with white band on secondaries. Bands missing from coverts on secondaries. Tertiaries grey stipple with brown outer edge. Scapulars grey stipple, smaller scapulars claret on outer edge. Tail white outer feathers, central feathers light grey, under tail charcoal-blue. Bill green with black bean. Eyes brown.

Duck's plumage : Head brown with charcoal-grey graining, faint eye stripe, light cream throat, 3/4 white neck ring incomplete at back. Breast, flanks & back rich brown with narrow charcoal-grey pencilling on upper breast, shoulders, back and upper flanks. Underbody pale cream with charcoal-grey flecking. Wings blue-grey frosting on flights, upper secondaries tinged with brown. Lower secondaries frosted as flights. Speculum as drake. Tail cream with grey frosting darkening to centre. Upper rump frosted with grey pencilling, feathers edged with brown. Bill dark orange with brown saddle. Legs brown.

The Light Blue Silver

Drake's plumage: Head charcoal-blue with white collar encircling neck. Breast claret, each feather laced with white, claret split by more white on lower breast. Back light grey with dark grey frosting, shading to charcoal-blue on rump. Flanks light claret feathers edged with white along upper, lower and belly white. Wings flights white, speculum charcoal-blue with white band on secondaries, bands missing from coverts of secondaries. Tertiaries grey stipple with browner outer edge. Scapulars grey stipple, smaller scapulars claret outer edge. Tail; white outer feathers, with light grey centre, undertail charcoal-blue. Bill green with black bean. Eyes brown.

Duck's plumage: Head white with charcoal-blue graining. No eye stripes. Body white with charcoal-blue mottling more pronounced on upper body and breast, light charcoal-blue mottling on back. Wing flights white, speculum light charcoal-blue, tertiaries and coverts carrying more colour than back. Tail white outer feathers, centre feathers lightly mottled with charcoal blue. Bill light orange with brown saddle. Eyes brown.

Silver Calls explained

The easiest way to understand how to differentiate between Silver, Apricot Silver and Blue Silver drakes is as follows:- The standard Silver drake is a Silver version of the Mallard, therefore, having a beetle-green head. The Apricot Silver drake is a Silver version of the Apricot, therefore, having a silvery-grey head, and the Blue Silver is a Silver version of the Blue Fawn, therefore having a charcoal-grey head. So if you know the standard colours, the silvers are not that complicated.

All the Silver drakes have the same characteristic of claret feathers extending along the flanks. The main difference between a normal Silver drake and a Dark Silver drake is the claret breast feathers which are much darker on the Dark Silver and the light-grey frosted feathers which extend down the flanks and right under the belly. These are the main differences between light and dark drakes and should make it easier for most people to see the differences. In all Dark Silvers the birds overall are much darker.

This is exactly the same for all non-standard Silvers, e.g. Apricot Silver and Blue Silver which come in normal and dark, the same as standard silvers. Silver Call drakes have many points to watch for which will cause problems with breeding top Calls. Starting at the head, there should be no white feathers in the beetle green head colour. The places to look are under the bill where white patches can appear when the birds moult into their breeding plumage and also be aware of white eye streaks.

The next place to look for trouble is on the rump. The back should be light grey with black frosting shading to black with a beetle-green sheen on the rump. You can find that shading extends too far onto the rump and also that the under rump has the same problems. Another fault is white flight feathers. The above problems also apply to the Apricot Silver and Blue Silver.
GRAHAM BARNARD

Chapter 7 - Preventing Disease

I do believe ducks are happier living out 24 hours a day in that they feel safer being able to see all around them. They are adequately provided with an overcoat designed to protect and keep them warm in all weathers. It not only keeps them warm but also dry, providing they are kept in good clean conditions with clean water. Fatalities in severe weather happen to birds that are not one hundred per cent fit and cannot cope. One should aim for a fit flock not a flock that only survives because it is coddled. The winter, in the wild, sorts out the weak from the strong ensuring that only the fittest are bred from to perpetuate a species. This is as it should be for reproducing weak birds can only lower the status of a flock and lead to its eventual failure.

Clean water is imperative for healthy ducks. You can see the water on top of this Call's feathers which are protected by its natural oils preventing the feathers getting wet.

Birds with wet feather very often have this problem because they are not on clean ground and do not have the means to keep themselves clean. Very old birds that are failing will develop this condition as the life force weakens. It is caused by the oil gland situated on the upper back, in front of the tail, malfunctioning either from being clogged up, infected or because it simply cannot cope. Affected birds preen obsessively but cannot put their plumage in order. They look reasonably fit until it rains or they enter the water, a thing they are reluctant to do with this condition as, with no waterproofing, they become wet to the skin and in severe weather become badly chilled. If one has a bird with chronic wet feather it is debatable whether it can be cured. Ensuring that the area where the bird is kept is mud free and that there is a supply of clean water helps. If it is a prized specimen it can be kept in but waterfowl as a general rule do not appreciate permanent incarceration and there comes a time when it is necessary to let it out again. Keeping waterfowl clean when housed is a tedious business and labour intensive. Clean they must be kept for most times the condition has been caused by poor management. Stress can be the reason for the condition and in some instances the bird will moult itself to perfect plumage once again. Excessively wet weather may result in the back feathers becoming a trifle wet but as soon as the deluge abates, given a few days, everything will be returned to order by the bird itself with no outside help at all. Clean ground and clean water are the order of the day.

Ailments

There are numerous ailments that your birds may or may not contract. I believe it is unnecessary for me to go into them in depth for if you notice more than one of your birds ailing or find more than one of your birds dead the first thing to be done will be to consult a Vet. The Call duck is bred by hobbyists and it is unlikely that any highly infectious disease will be experienced. For those who import birds from abroad these birds will be kept in quarantine away from your main flock until such time as it can be seen that no serious disease is present.

Call Ducks, in general, suffer from few ailments but, as with all waterfowl, do not show signs of illness until the later stages. Stockmanship must play its part in keeping your flock healthy. Overcrowding will reap its own misfortunes and which of us is not overcrowded at the end of the breeding season. Fortunately nature has ordained that the weather during the season, i.e. the summer, is conducive to being able to sustain large numbers of birds, on relatively little space, for a short period of time. Should the summer be wet, as was this summer of 1998, life becomes trying. Mud does not benefit young ducks at all and can cause various problems. It is tempting to keep young ducks indoors after the time they should be put out with disastrous results, for, unfortunately, overcrowding inside can be as detrimental as overcrowding outside. Cleanliness is the answer both inside and out. Keep the rearing pens clean by adding fresh bedding as many times a day as necessary and keep the birds outside supplied with clean water. Mud can be soaked up with a variety of substances. Sand, shavings or, in a dire emergency, turf.

Young birds kept in dirty, wet conditions are susceptible to wet feather. Wet feather is caused by the preen gland situated on the back directly in front of the tail failing to produce oil. This gland produces the oil which enables the duck to stay waterproofed. The bird can be seen, when preening, rubbing its chin over this gland and distributing the oil to its feathers. Should the gland malfunction the feathers do not remain oiled. While the bird can avoid entering water it cannot stay dry in heavy rain. The bird will become wet and stay wet unless the weather is favourable. It will become chilled in very cold weather. It will, in muddy conditions, become a very sorry sight and no amount of preening, which it does obsessively, will put it right. The bird which can be housed inside and given only drinking water will in time recover but once put outside it will again become dirty and wet. Birds that are housed for any length of time show the same symptoms when released but, given time, will re-oil themselves. I believe some birds develop wet feather when stressed. Wet, stinking pens can be classed as stress. Old birds become bedraggled also but this is due to age. A broad based antibiotic can be administered but the cure is to clean your act up and replan your strategy.

It is the young bird that is the most vulnerable and ducklings can and do fall ill. The odd sickly bird can be treated with a broad based antibiotic obtainable from your local Veterinary Surgeon. As most vets do not specialise in poultry it is as well to suggest to them that a broad based antibiotic will perhaps do the trick. This is best administered in the water so a powder which is water soluble will be supplied. I find that a drinker which does not disgorge its contents too readily is best for ducks do love to play with water. You do not need your medicine to end up on the floor instead of inside the patient.
If the recommended dosage is that it be given for 5 consecutive days make sure that this is done. I also suggest that on day 1 you double the recommended dose hitting whatever ails them hard.

Sinus

Perhaps the complaint, if it can be called a complaint, which obsesses Call Duck breeders the most is the incidence of sinus problems in their stock. This takes the form of enlarged cheeks. Squeezing the cheeks causes a clear mucus to run out of the nostrils. Much has been said about sinus and how to cure it but I fear the fact remains that it is something of a mystery. One thing is certain, it does not kill a bird nor seemingly affect it, apart from the fact that it is disfiguring and prevents the bird from being shown. It is also more prevalent in the better Calls and, therefore, it is exasperating to have your best youngster for the year develop it. There do not seem to be any hard and fast rules as to which bird is going to be prone to it and never have I experienced an epidemic. One cannot even say that a particular brood or the offspring of a particular pair will be affected but, rather, odd birds. As might be expected, the birds that do have it tend to wheeze and birds cured continue to wheeze. This probably indicates some degree of congestion in the lungs or perhaps some mucus present in the sinus cavities. Sinuses that become infected will turn the clear mucus present a brownish colour and it is but a short step to this setting solid. I once owned an Apricot duck which lived to be over 10 years of age, laying and producing to the end. She was infected on one side only and was very ugly to observe. I have also owned a Mallard duck which had a very slight case of sinus trouble which strangely disappeared each year when she was incubating a clutch of eggs. One could conclude from this that the passage of water through the nostrils in some way encourages the sinus to thrive.

This little duck has a sinus problem in one of her cheeks and needs treating.

Treating.

If you can catch the incidence of sinus infection early enough I believe it is quite possible to cure but it must be spotted early and it must be dealt with at once. The medicine recommended is Tylan 200 and must be obtained from your Vet. Tylan can be obtained in injectable form and in water soluble form. I recommend that the water soluble form be used and that one confines the bird to a small run and ensures that it has only the dosed water available. I also recommend that if after the full course has been given, if no immediate improvement can be seen after a break of about a week, the whole course is repeated with the initial dose being doubled. Tylan is not the only medicine which can be used and one should put oneself in the hands of the Vet.

Lameness

Birds can become lame for various reasons and to varying degrees. Should one have been chasing birds for any length of time it is possible one or two may give the appearance of having become lame. Left overnight and with no further disturbance they will be seen to recover. Birds that have been stressed by being boxed and introduced to new surroundings can become lame and it is best to put these birds into a pen which is quiet with food and water for a period of time. It is not recommended that the bird be left in a box, for this in itself can cause stress and care must be taken to ensure that the bird is eating and drinking. Lameness seems to be more common in the breeding season and this is due in part to increased activity. If one observes them on the pond when fresh water has been provided one cannot wonder that they sometimes knock themselves, incurring lameness, for they do throw themselves about in total abandonment. Occasionally there is a serious injury and the lameness continues. When this happens I place the bird in a pen with food and water on the back lawn. Each day I bring the bird in and put it on the bath which I fill with enough water to ensure that the bird cannot stand. A couple of hours per day with a weight taken off the injured leg and it is amazing how soon they will recover. Occasionally there is permanent damage to leg ligaments or tendons having been torn beyond repair and it is then best to cull the bird.

Worming

Unless one takes a sample of faeces to be analysed one can never really be sure that one's birds have worms or not although I have read that it is possible to detect the presence of tape worm in one's birds when one vent sexes them. It is, therefore, best to assume that one has worms and to treat them twice a year. If they are wormed in the autumn, enabling them to face

110

the rigours of the winter, and again in the spring this will give them the best start they can have for the breeding season. Worms debilitate a bird and, should there be any latent infection waiting to be triggered, it will be able to gain a foothold as the condition of the bird deteriorates. If one is overstocked and has worms present the incidence of reinfection will be high.

It is quite possible for a bird to live quite happily with a latent infection wait ing to be triggered. If there is no stress it will live and breed. Once the stress has occurred the resistance of the bird is lowered and it will become ill.

Lice

Whilst chickens seem to suffer from any number of creepy crawlies ducks do not appear to accumulate quite so many but do have their fair share. Feather lice can be seen on the wings flattened along the flight feathers and, presumably, ducks that are housed nightly have more parasites than those which live out. As we are no longer able to buy Cooper's Louse powder which most of us were very familiar with and which we all used to shake about madly I now use a Dog Flea Spray as recommended by an older vet. No doubt this is also frowned on but if it is used in the open air and a quick squirt is made down the back and under the wings the lice and anything else are put paid to. At the time when Cooper's Louse Powder was taken off the market, for whatever reason, there did not appear to be any alternative offered. It was, therefore, necessary to use whatever one found was beneficial. If there is a preparation on the market today I, for one, am unaware of it.

Houses can be gone over with a flame thrower and if the straw in nestboxes is set alight and care is taken, the box is scorched out and anything living in it is killed. Occasionally towards the end of the season when the weather has been hot and muggy it will be found that the nest boxes are infested with fleas. These appear to resemble those found on domestic pets. If one finds the eggs covered in little brown spots this is blood which has come from the bird when the flea has taken its fill. A good blast with the flea spray when the bird is off the nest will put paid to this and I have not so far lost any birds after such a treatment. Nor I may add have they deserted. I can only assume that they are so relieved to find the nest rid of these irritating pests that is does not occur to them that anything has happened to necessitate desertion. I also keep a can of the preparation which one uses in the house if one owns cats and dogs and treat the hen house with this if red mite or fleas are present. To date no ill effects have been noticed.

Chapter 8 - Predators

Four Legged Furred Predators

Foxes can cause havoc in the duck pen. They come by night or by day. I often hear of ducks being taken during day light hours but in most instances it is birds that have whole fields to roam in that are taken and usually when they are farthest away from human habitation. Birds that are in a controlled area will get taken in daylight but there is less likelihood. Birds left out all night when they should have been shut up are very vulnerable should the fox decide to make his rounds. Houses can be broken into if they have a weak spot and fences dug under or jumped over. Electric fencing does help but do keep it switched on. During the growing season it does not take too much time either to cut back vegetation or to spray along the ground level wire with weed killer. Today's preparations are usually neutralised when they come in contact with the ground or after they have dried on the plant. I have been using a particular herbicide for many years and did in fact once observe a drake drinking it from a dock leaf. No, he did not die but he gave me palpitations for a day or two!

The one thing a raid from the fox does is show you where your weak spots are. If you do not immediately take steps to strengthen your defences then you must be prepared for future losses. One thing is certain, should the fox enter there will be few birds left alive. He will go quite mad when he finds so many birds confined for his sport.

There are various methods of catching a fox, none of which your average duck keeper is an expert in. The best method of solving your problem is to speak to a local farmer who will know someone who specialises in the art of extermination. An art it is and best left to the expert.

Talking to a lady some time ago I was interested to hear that she had noticed an increase in the predation by foxes after local people had been issued with wheely bins by the local council. Deprived of access to dustbins the foxes were forced to look elsewhere for easy pickings. Urban foxes are probably more difficult to trap than rural foxes. The urban fox becomes adept at jumping over garden fences and walls while the rural fox is used to dig under. A trap can be placed inside a fence that has been dug under but catching the fox that comes over is a different matter. With electric fencing both at the top of the fence and again at the bottom one does keep the fox at bay most of the time. This fence should be serviced regularly. All vegetation should be cut back away from the wire and any ticking investigated. Vigilance is required for the fox will show you no mercy and there will be no second chance.

Rodents

Rats have the habit of moving in with great stealth. The first we know of them is either that they have killed some young stock or there are holes being dug everywhere with houses chewed. Tremendous damage can be experienced when the presence of rats is neglected. They will dig in and settle down to breed. Before one knows it houses are damaged and duck runs overrun. The story of the Pied Piper of Hamlyn is based on a true phenomenon in that rats will suddenly take it in their heads to move en masse. My husband travelling along a country lane came upon a lady trapped in her car while hundreds of rats crossed the road around her. It was an awesome sight for the road was covered with a living mass of grey bodies. How many there were it is impossible to assess but obviously they had exhausted the resources where they had been living and were looking for a new home. During my childhood my parents experienced a large influx of rats when the local grain merchant cleared out his premises. We lived at the time in a pub which had been a coaching house. The old stables, which were built of cob were still in existence, the rats dug in everywhere and the area was redolent of rotting rats which had died within the thick cob walls. The damage was extensive and it took many pounds of poison and quite a time to clear them all out.

Over a period of time one becomes familiar with where they usually take up residence and it is a simple matter to check these sites from time to time and put down a supply of poison. This should be checked each day and added to as and when it has been consumed. I find bait will be taken for approximately five days by which time it has become effective within the system and the rat dies. Should there be several it may take much longer as each rat will need to eat sufficient. Care should be taken that this is placed for the consumption of the rat only. Many a dog has been rushed to the vet having helped itself. Traps can be set for the rat quite successfully but they are caught alive and have to be disposed of. To this end an air rifle is a handy weapon to have. It is possible to drown them but I feel not even a rat deserves to meet its end in this way.

If you own a cat it will catch the odd rat but it is a very good cat that will take on an adult rat. Once they have acquired the knack they will be a help but no matter how good the cat it will not solve the problem entirely. The same can be said for a good dog. Most of the Terriers were bred to help control predators of one sort or another. There is nothing quite like ratting with your own dog and it is great fun. However the rat does not loiter to be caught and there is a large element of chance. A supply of poison is a much surer way of eliminating rats.

I have heard it said if you have mice you will not have rats. I must say that since I finally caught the last rat in my duck runs the incidence of mice has increased dramatically. For 12 months I baited poison as rat after rat appeared on the scene. As fast as I dispatched one another arrived. I solved the problem as to where they were coming from when one of my neighbours informed me she had had them but they had gone away and another told me she had acquired some cats to get rid of the rats. In the first instance the rats had not gone away but had dug in and were busily reproducing. When I met the same neighbour sometime later I was relieved to hear that they had been putting down a supply of poison for their chicken food was fast disappearing. As to the neighbour who acquired the cats I suspect I dispatched the rats myself.

It is as well to take steps to dispose of mice as well as rats. They too can cause havoc and where they leave their faeces and urine on food this can be extremely detrimental to our birds. My cats are forever coming in with mice and voles but they do not hunt in my duck runs. One of them does hunt in the tunnel greenhouse and surrounds. Upon hearing a chicken in some distress one evening I went to investigate. The cat was asleep on the bench and the chicken wanted to go to roost!

Stoats And Weasels

Stoats and Weasels are extremely difficult to keep out of the duck run for being so small they can walk through your fence. Keeping a few pheasants in the run with your ducks will help pinpoint their presence for they will hunt these first and you will know you have a problem when they begin to be killed. They can be caught in a cage trap and released well away from your land. They are, in some places, becoming increasingly rare and little is heard of them nowadays. Talking to a very good wildfowl breeder some years ago he told me he had caught 22 weasels by one hollow tree with one egg. I rather suspect we should be pushed to find one weasel today unless we were living well out in the country. If this is not the case no doubt I shall hear soon enough.

Mink are a real enemy for they are unafraid of man. One wonders if they are afraid of anything. For those of us who do not live near running water there is little fear of a visit by the mink but for those of us that do there is every chance that we shall come across them at some time. I do not think there is a river in the country that does not have the mink on it now. Recently I did read in a daily newspaper that the otter is making a comeback and was not decimated by the advent of the mink but by pesticides. It seems that the otter is well able to defend itself and it is to be hoped that it will, given time, reduce the mink numbers significantly.

The mink can do most things but it does not burrow well so there is little fear that it will dig itself into the duck run. It can swim, climb, dive and follows water. It can, however, go through any hole of more than one and quarter inches in diameter. It is as destructive as the fox in that it kills anything it can get its teeth into, sinking them into the back of the neck behind the head and leaving the bird with not a mark upon it. To ascertain the cause of death the back of the neck should be plucked where two puncture marks either side will be found.

To catch the mink is easy once you have discovered the right place for the trap. They are best caught with a cage trap which is covered to represent a hole. They cannot resist investigating a hole and while you can bait the trap it is not really necessary. The first thing you need to discover is the best place to site the trap and then it is a matter of leaving it there tilled at all times. You will need to check it for you will catch any number of other things, including the neighbour's cat, should the trap be baited with something it fancies, but then again you may wish to catch the neighbour's cat. It is the discovering of the best place to set your trap that can be costly in the number of birds lost but once you have found it, given a little luck, you will not lose any more birds as the mink will be caught before he can do any damage.

Once you have your mink in the trap be particularly careful for they are extremely vicious and unafraid. Even if you own a good terrier, it is not wise to expect it to dispatch a mink unless it is familiar with them. The best of dogs is taken aback when a mink screams its head off and rushes at it. The vermin we have in this country usually run away. Once a dog has acquired the expertise to dispatch a mink it does so as it would a rat but the learning process can be painful.

While mink can strike at any time of the year March/ April and September/ October are the most dangerous months. In March and April they are moving around seeking mates while in September and October the young are sent out into the world to fend for themselves. Seeking a territory of their own and not being experts at fending for themselves, if they come upon your premises they have found an easy source of food.

There are many tales told which illustrate the ferocity of mink and while Area Representative for Devon for the British Waterfowl Association I invited the Master of the Devon & Cornwall Mink Hounds to come one evening to give us a talk. The Mink Hound was once the Otter Hound but the Hunt Masters, when the otter became scarce, changed their quarry to the mink as 'they are the real enemy.' The Otter/Mink Hound is a large shaggy black and tan animal with a waterproof outer coat under which is a dense undercoat. It has large webbed feet which enable it to swim strongly. Hunting is done during the summer months when the level of the water in the rivers is low, for the hounds hunt the river banks. The huntsmen follow behind the hounds in the river.

Mink will take birds from outside the back door or in the stream at the bottom of the garden in broad daylight. They will enter your house and will attack you or your dogs. A gentleman recently told me the tale of a gamekeeper who, with his three terriers, was releasing a cage caught mink in the middle of a field. Asked whether it would get away he replied - it would not. While he was opening the cage his dogs decided to fight for the privilege of dispatching the quarry and the mink tore across the field and climbed a nearby tree. Laughing helplessly, the spectator challenged the Gamekeeper that he had said it would not get away. 'It will not,' he replied fetching his gun from the Landrover!

Badger

The Ministry of Agriculture will not agree that Badgers kill poultry. There are many people who would argue with this claim and, should you be unfortunate enough to suffer an attack from a badger and seek help from your local Wildlife Group, they are likely to arrive with a cage, bait it with bread and honey and advise you, if you catch the badger, you will need to be quick or it will escape again. I do not think there is any way, apart from bricks and mortar or heavy steel to keep a badger out if he has decided to enter. The strength of these creatures is immense and should not be underestimated. As the badger was not designed to kill for his living it is unfortunate that where he catches your bird he will begin to eat. Fortunately, it is not often that you will sustain an attack but in hot dry weather the badger is pushed to find his natural food and it is then that he will turn to, what is for him, an unnatural diet. He will, however, kill everything in the pen given the opportunity. If you are fortunate enough to catch him alive he can be transported many miles away. The law is such that you are unable to kill him for he is protected. I read recently that the Ministry is to resume the slaughter of badgers so it will be in your own best interests to contact them if necessary. More than once the badger has been found in a shed surrounded by his carnage fast asleep. Should you be able to arrange for the Ministry man to arrive before he wakes up what better chance of proving my point!

Feathered Predators

Crows, Jackdaws, Magpies, etc. are a continuing problem. It seems that no sooner one dispatches one egg eater in the Spring than another appears on the scene. Well placed nest boxes with screens over their entrances do help to mitigate predation by birds. Throwing eggs over the fence to lie on open ground is an invitation to the local bird population that you have eggs and they will not be slow to take advantage of the fact. While ample vegetation helps, high trees nearby are used as lookout posts. Crows, etc. will sit in the tree and spy out the land. They will watch where the duck goes to lay and when she has left the nest will fly down to sample the still warm egg. That they seemingly just puncture the egg and leave most of it behind is exasperating. That they will empty a newly discovered nest spoiling all the clutch is infuriating.

Ducklings that are put out unprotected at a young age are a treat also and to find umpteen bodies which have been pecked about, the heads lying everywhere, is devastating.

Broody ducks will defend their eggs when a bird attempts to entice them away from the nest but they are fighting a losing battle for as they rise up to attack the bird will have an egg from under them. The whole clutch can be lost and you none the wiser, for disturbing the broody duck is not recommended. Finding an egg lying outside a nest box I investigated to find the duck wounded directly above her eye still sitting tight. She had put up a good fight. I removed the remaining eggs into safe keeping. The wound healed over a period of time but the sight in the eye was lost.

I have tried numerous methods of scaring crows etc. away. At certain times of the year when the young have flown they, like the young mink, are looking for easy pickings, being not quite adept at fending for themselves. They discover where you feed your birds and in a short space of time empty the food containers after you have left the area. A plastic bag hung over the feeder which fills in the wind or just hangs there will be effective for about a week but as your birds will pass under it to feed it does not take the crow long to realise there is nothing to worry about. I have even hung up disposable overalls to loom over the run but again they were only effective for a short space of time. I received a fright when walking past in the twilight as they sat up a tree and pondered. Whatever clever device you fashion is soon ineffective. The only truly effective method is to dispatch as many of these birds as you can. To this end, if you don't own a gun the Larsen Trap is the answer. Do remember when firing a gun that lead pellets which have fallen within the range of your birds will, if picked up by them, settle in the gizzard and be ground up with the ingested food. Lead will circulate in the system of the bird and lead poisoning will result. This can be fatal. It is best to fire only at those birds situated where the shot will fall outside the duck run.

The basic Larsen Trap has two compartments. One in which to catch your bird and one to keep your decoy bird in. The catching side has a split perch holding open the spring loaded door. When a bird lands on this perch it collapses releasing the door and entrapping the bird. Catching the first bird is the difficult part and the trap should be baited accordingly. When you are losing eggs an egg is necessary to catch the culprit. A faster less frustrating method is to make a phone call and locate the person who has already caught some and obtain one of his spares. The bird is placed in the keeping department and is fed and watered. This bird is important for he is the decoy. It is he who calls to those flying about who investigate because he is a stranger, fly down to defend their territory and land on the split perch which collapses releasing the spring. The door snaps shut securing them. Usually if the first bird caught is a crow you will continue to catch crows but should you catch a magpie, as well as trapping other magpies, it is possible to catch a crow for they will fly in to attack it. Seemingly everybody dislikes a magpie. Once the holding side of the trap has several birds in you must then dispose of some for, apart from lack of space, they eat quantities of food. I learnt this year that money had been asked for a decoy bird. I should have to be desperate before I paid for my first bird. Enterprising it might be to charge for this service but we are all in the same boat and surely it is war we have declared. To pay money to wage it is, to me, immoral.

Birds Of Prey

Over the years I have lost young birds to Buzzards which posed something of a problem for they are a protected species. The birds in question nested high in the trees at the top of a neighbouring field. I solved the problem by tying lengths of cord across the pen, tying cut up strips of plastic feed bag to it. These gave us a rather festive appearance and did solve the problem. It is usually partly grown birds which are taken for they are easily transportable. These birds do not kill for pleasure but take one meal at a time.

A pair of Apricot Calls, blissfully happy swimming in thier pond/sand pit in the sunshine.

On very rare occasions owls also can prey on our young birds. Each parent will take a bird and each night they will return if they are feeding young. Again one has one's hand tied for they are also protected.

The answer must lie in keeping our juvenile birds within an area that can be protected by covering the run with plastic netting. It is not usual for adult birds to suffer the same fate as young birds.

Domestic Cats

While it is almost impossible to keep a badger out when it has decided to enter, the domestic cat must rate top of the list when it comes to keeping it out of a duck run fenced to keep everything else out. I had never succeeded in keeping my own cats out before the advent of the electric fence and only succeeded afterwards by catching them inside the wire and throwing them in the duck ponds. Certain of my cats have persisted, thumbing their nose at me no doubt, but usually leaving my birds alone. The stray cat or the neighbour's cat is the problem. If you have cats of your own they will keep stray cats away for most of the time. The one saving factor with predation by a cat is that it will kill only one bird at a time. It may come back and take one every day but it will be one at a time. Catching a cat is fairly easy especially if it is a stray or a cat that has been dumped. I have in my time had numerous cats dumped in the neighbourhood, usually entire tom cats, who have visited my establishment. The problem can be solved quite easily. If the cat has been dumped it still has no fear of humans and can be enticed by being fed. Once caught, the local Cats' Protection League will take it, neuter it and re-home it.

The cat of a certain neighbour did visit me once and I had evil intentions towards it. Its owner never could understand why, when I entered her house, George left post haste through the cat flap. As cats usually like me I can only assume that the waves of aggression that emitted from me whenever I saw him gave him some clue as to my intentions. He lived to be a ripe old age and did not enter my premises but once.

Stray cats that are wary are usually hungry and are also easily caught by baiting a trap with something tasty. In fact the local Cats' Protection League will be able to supply this trap for they use them to clear industrial sites etc.

Other Predators

There seems to be no end to the ways in which you can lose your precious birds and seemingly no way in which you can be absolutely sure you have done everything you can to ensure their safety. While there are the known predators with fur and four legs and with feathers and two legs, many of us have experienced the loss of birds to the two legged non-feathered variety, and it must be said that success at the shows can bring this abomination down upon one. Some shows do not print exhibitors' addresses in their catalogues but all in all it is not very difficult for your whereabouts to be located. When I sustained a loss of birds I was horrified to learn that a reporter from a local paper had been looking for me and further horrified when my neighbour asked me if it was true I had had birds stolen as this reporter had arrived on his doorstep. The reporter didn't find me but the Police had given out sufficient information for a news item to be included in the next edition of the local paper.

Natural coverage with trees can be aided with wire mesh for protection of your ducks, as these Miniature Silver Appleyards show

When one sustains a loss in this way it is extremely upsetting for, when all is said and done, it has to be someone who knows you and whom you know and whom you have shown around the property. People do not come with ill intent if they do not know where they are going. As it is usually your better birds that disappear this fact is underlined. The most horrifying tale I ever heard was the theft of all one person's female Calls. While one can replace a drake, finding spare ducks must constitute the worst scenario ever.
A friend once had the Police visit as they had been informed that her name had been mentioned in circles where it should not have been. Their advice was to put padlocks on all her external gates and keep them locked at all times. Should she then find somebody in her duck pens she would know the person should not be there. If the gates were not locked and she

chanced to come upon trespassers they need only say they were looking and nothing could be done. She was also advised to vary her shopping days, telling no one when she was going and if she went on holiday keep that a closely guarded secret. It seems incredible to me that such lengths should be needed but it is a fact of life that there are those out there who will steal time from you. I say time for the monetary value of our birds is relatively small. Although a large flock can amount to a significant figure it is unlikely that all of it will be stolen at once. But it can take several years to build up a flock of Calls that are producing well and the loss can be irretrievable. This puts us in a difficult position for naturally we want to show our birds to various people and personally I have no idea what a crook looks like. It seems we take a chance every time we show a stranger over our flock and property. It is a decision for the individual but a well planted pen does hide the majority of the birds from view.

A Mallard female call, exhibited by John Kay and Son

In the past there were several birds that disappeared at the actual shows. Show organisers began to seek ways to minimise the risk for indeed they were in danger of losing entries. Security varies from one show to another but on the whole it is good. When the time comes to box up the birds for the return journey home the doors of the stadium are closed and it is not until all exhibitors have boxed their birds and no one has found a bird to be missing that the doors are opened. If there is sufficient space, exhibitors are asked to leave their boxes within the building, again minimising the risk of theft. It is quite easy to pick up a bird in the cage next to yours and be unaware that you have done it. It is the disappearance from a cage of a bird that has the distinction of being individual i.e. one bird in a particular class that just happens to be across the aisle from the rest, that one does ponder.

Chapter 9 - Breed Summary of the Ideal Call

There is a standard brought out by the B.W.A. as to just what one is supposed to aim for when breeding the perfect Call. As we all interpret this standard in our own way so Call ducks vary. This is what makes the showing of any bird or animal worth while for if we all interpreted the standard in the same way we should know before we went to the show who was going to win and, therefore, would have given up long ago. It is what each one of us decides pleases our eye that decides for us what we are aiming at.

The standard is there to tell us what constitutes a fault and what we should avoid at all costs. Some of us breed for the head alone and, therefore, forget the body. Some of us breed for the body and hope to get the head. Ideally we should breed for both as both are equally difficult. The number of points allocated for colour has recently been reduced thus lessening the urgency to breed true colours. With the advent of so many new colours in the Calls we must ensure that we do not lose the true colours by giving names to mismarked birds. Every bird or strain of birds has its weaknesses or faults and the object must be to try to breed these weaknesses and faults out of them. Whatever we seek to eliminate we shall not do it in one season.

Should we have too long a body this can be rectified by bringing in a bird with a short body, but to produce a flock of short bodied birds will only be done over a number of years and care must be taken that we do not lose the one feature in which our birds excel. Each successive breeding season the best of the bunch is retained and bred back to the birds with the points we wish to retain in our own flock. A bird with a long body, and a poor head which is over sized is unlikely to produce a small bird with a good head and a short body. Put to a bird with these attributes, one or more of the offspring will show signs of those points we are trying to achieve and, given time and thought, successive generations will show improvements. Never think that you will ever reach a stage when every duckling you breed will be a show winner for each and every season there will be that throwback to remind you of your beginnings.

Broadly speaking, a Call duck should be round, deep and short. Round head. round body, round eye. Deep domed forehead, deep body. Short, broad beak, short neck, short legs, short body.

A Call Duck's Ability to Adapt

I have no doubt that there are many people who, having seen Call ducks at an exhibition, have gone home with the desire to keep some of them, but have felt that the space which they had available was inadequate. This may not always be the case as shown by the following information which is based on a video, filmed in America and showing a family of Call ducks living happily in the middle of a housing estate.

A sand pit in a rural garden but this time the owner Evelyn has put pebbles round the sides to prevent the ducks making the outside muddy.

In this instance there was only a very small area of grass available, the rest of their habitat was constructed in concrete, stone and wood. (Watching this film made me realise how simple it was to include Call ducks in a landscaping project.) The area used was at the rear of a house which quickly rose into a series of plateaux, where small ponds had been constructed. The main pool was at ground level from which the water was pumped to the highest plateau where its descent was directed through a series of waterfalls, each one feeding the small ponds until it eventually reached the main pond ready to be recirculated to the summit. The main pond was surrounded by gravel for the ducks to use as a drying off area.

These miniature waterfalls were often used by the ducks as slides illustrating that when you are constructing them they should not be at too steep an angle. Their house was a miniature 'log cabin', not built at ground level but set back into the hillside. It was quite large and like a log cabin, built of barked timber. Obviously common ply boarding would be sufficient but in this case the project had been built as a showpiece. Even the front door had brass handles and a 'Harley Street' door knocker.

The floor was wooden and bedded with straw. The house itself was raised from the ground with access to it via a short staircase. The steps were close together and the ducks climbed them with ease. The birds were fed a staple diet of top quality compound. This was in pellet form and offered to them in dishes which were placed in several areas around their compound.

Decoration and a little shade were provided by plants and shrubs which were growing in large decorative pots strategically placed around the area. Their small grass area was surrounded by a conifer type of bush. These acted as both shade from the sun and as a windbreak. Care was taken not to feed the birds on the lawn, thus keeping damage to the minimum. This area also offers the ducks a natural environment in which to make a nest and lay their clutch of eggs. However, some of them preferred to lay in their 'home', rather than under a well foliaged bush.

The ones which favoured their house had several options open to them. Initially the house had been built as a two storey building, but later a third floor had been added with the upper bedroom including several nesting boxes. Some of them were open topped whilst others were more enclosed with a front entrance, as in wildfowl laying boxes. Access to the two floors was again by a low stepped 'staircase'. At dusk the ducks were shut away in their home and the pump switched off, thus reducing the noise level to a minimum. The only maintenance for the 'duck pen' is that, periodically, the pump was switched off and all the concrete area brushed down into the pond, which was then drained and the residue shovelled into a small barrow ready for disposal.

The depth of detail in which you could extend both the internal and external design of their dwelling is endless, but I can assure you that the Calls will appreciate all your efforts. They really are nosy characters who want to be included in all your everyday activities. One advantage in using such a small enclosure is a great reduction in the risk of losing stock to predators as can be the case in more conventional environments.

The chapter heading refers to a Call duck's ability to adapt to different habitats. I can quote many instances where Calls have been successfully kept and bred in a small area of a garden without any running water or elaborate surroundings The basic requirements for such a pen is a bathing area which can be provided by a small sink or no longer used baby's bath. These containers do not need to be excessively deep, somewhere around six inches can be sufficient, providing that they are washed out and refilled with clean water daily. Ideally the bath should be situated on a gravel based area which provides a place for the birds to dry off when exiting from their playtime swim. Again, access to the 'pond' is by way of a small step ladder or length of board with bars across it enabling better grip for the birds' feet.

Calls love to play in the water but they must also be given a dry sleeping area where they can preen themselves and relax. I prefer this to be bedded with straw which is a natural commodity in which the birds can nestle down during cold weather.

Plants and grass give wonderful natural protection and can also enhance the look of your duck pen.

Small bushes or shrubs are very useful to act as shade from both wind and the sun. Their sleeping quarters do not require to be anything more than fox proof and draught proof, but this does not need to be totally enclosed. A steady flow of fresh air directed well above the birds' heads is very beneficial to good health.

The main drawback to this system is during a spell of wet weather when the pen quickly turns into a 'slutch patch', which is slow to recover into a good grass sward. The problem can usually be prevented by limiting the number of birds kept. It is very easy to become overstocked during the summer when conditions should be perfect, but as winter approaches these ideal conditions rapidly deteriorate.

This chapter has been included in the book as a way of assuring prospective 'Call keepers' that they do not have to own a large lake and an acre of meadowland with a stream running through to enjoy the pleasures of breeding small ducks.

The Magical Eclipse.

At this time of the year, mother nature carries out one of many unique, and often underestimated acts of routine procedures.
In breeds of Waterfowl, such as Mallard and their enlarged developments, like the Rouen etc., all male birds have natural plumage of highly striking colours, including delicate shades of grey and iridescent blue.
In the wild, the moulting of these birds' wing feathers would leave them unable to fly away from predators, who would be quickly attracted to their bright colouring. Consequently, 'Mother Nature' gives these birds an intermediate covering of feathers which are camouflage colouring, as in the females' natural plumage. Once the drake has regrown his wing feathers, this drab colouring is replaced with the bird's original decorative and very attractive looking contrast of colours.
From an exhibition breeder's point of view, when the Rouen drake moults into eclipse, the lacing to his feathers varies in standard perfection.
Some males show very little lacing, and would be considered more of a drake breeding strain, whilst others show double lacing, or pencilling, as it is often called, as good as that of a female of show quality. These drakes were the ones used as breeders in the duck breeding pen by many of the old specialist Waterfowl Exhibitors.

The Black East Indian.

Introduction

In all the breeds of duck there is probably nothing more striking than a correctly plumaged Black East Indian, especially when seen in full bloom sailing on a pond and glistening in the sunlight. This correct colouring can best be described as iridescent beetle green and the really top quality show birds carry this green sheen through under their breast and tail. Inferior quality stock carry a purple tinge to their top colour spoiling the breed's main feature which carries a massive 30 points in the club standard for B.E.I.

The B.E.I. has been bred and shown in this country since the nineteenth century. Unfortunately its popularity declined around the 1980s due to the newly created interest in showing Mandarin, Carolina, Teal etc. This decline was also noticed in the Call Duck exhibits.

This reproduction was taken from the book 'The Illustrated Book of Domestic Poultry by Martin Doyle', printed in 1854.

Discussion surrounding the origin of both the Cayuga and the B.E.I. has been so long and complicated that we have dealt with it as a separate part of this breed summary. That there is a relationship between the two breeds would appear to have very sound ground in any debate. Their ability to lay dark grey or even black coloured eggs at the commencement of a laying cycle being one point. In both breeds, the females especially tend to moult with white feathers in the body plumage. This tends to increase in area each year. Not all birds do this and by careful selection of breeding stock the fault can be restricted. Unfortunately, it is often the ones which showed the superior colouring when in their first year which develop the phenomenon.

Another pointer is that in many of the early writings about the two breeds special mention is made of the unique flavour of their meat when eaten. Apparently, black ducks were extensively bred as commercial table ducklings during the nineteenth century.

The section dealing with the history and possible origin of the B.E.I. highlights many writers' different views. However, at this point, I am relating a piece written by Arthur Doyle in his book, *The Illustrated Book of Domestic Poultry*, which was published in 1852 and was under the heading of 'Black Labrador' ducks. This was one of the many descriptions used during the last century, when referring to black ducks.

This variety has gone under the names of Buenos Ayres duck and the Black East Indian duck. The Zoological Society first received it from Buenos Ayres, but it is known in the south of England by the last mentioned name, according to Mr Dixon who prefers this designation, from a belief that it was imported from India and probably via Buenos Ayres.

Mr Baker has advertised them under the first title. The plumage of a drake's body is black with a greenish purple shade to it and the bill is also black with a tinge of green. The neck, back and larger feathers of the tail and wings are lustrous with mineral green. The duck has a much plainer dress, yet tinged with the same colourings.

Two remarkable properties of this species are that, in the early part of the season, the duck lays black eggs, the shades of white gradually appearing in the subsequent laying until the ordinary colour succeeds. An oily matter which may be scraped off causes this discolouration. They lay a little later than other ducks but are as hardy and are superior in having a high wild duck flavour. Sometimes they moult white.

This species has been ranked under the domestication class, though it is questionable whether they are not rather occupying a middle place between the wild and tame. They are rather in a transition state from primitive freedom to confinement and the habits of domesticated life.

This brief breed description was written some 150 years ago and yet most of it is still correct, though it may well be that the colouring of the female has been improved. In many of the early descriptions of the breed, reference is made to some of the drakes having faulty brown colouring along their flanks. This point can still be present and should be severely down graded when judging and avoided in the breeding pen.

The present day B.E.I. has been standardised to weigh 2 lbs for drakes and $1^1/_2$ lbs for ducks, which is exactly the same as those quoted for the Silver Bantam Duck which Chris Ashton has described in another section of this book, and some $1/_2$lb heavier than the standard weight for Call Ducks.

In temperament, the B.E.I. is quite a shy bird, maybe even nervous in some of the blood lines and not really comparable to the friendly and inquisitive natured Call Duck. If the Indies are not pinioned i.e. full winged, the birds are strong in flight, but providing that they are well established in their habitat they return home after a quick fly round the surrounding area.

I quote here an extract from Harrison Weir's book 'Our Poultry', which was written just after the turn of the century - *Like my wild ducks (Mallards) the B.E.I. would fly off in the evening but always returned with them after a short time, this exercise of the wings probably conduced to the size of their pectoral muscles and thus helped to make them so valuable for culinary purposes.*

He also states that the B.E.I. often paired with the Mallards and reared healthy stock which had meaty breasts and a delicious flavour which could scarcely be surpassed.
In his book 'The East Indie Duck' which was written in America, Darrel Sheraw, who is one of the top waterfowl breeders in the U.S.A., says that the B.E.I. is quiet in temperament. This illustrates my point that their nature can vary between different strains and it is very noticeable when judging the birds.

The Origin Of The Black East Indian.

Anyone wishing to trace the origin of the B. E. I. will find the task either intriguing or frustrating, perhaps both. If you wish to speed the exercise, I suggest that you read the chapter in an American book called The East Indie Duck, written by Darrel Sheraw. A chapter on this subject covers 8 pages with the conclusion, 'There is no breed of domestic ducks whose origin is so shrouded in mystery as that of the East Indie'.

There are several issues to consider when debating the subject, one being the theory that all breeds of domestic ducks descend from the Mallard family, a pointer being that they all carry the peculiarity of having their central four tail feathers turning upwards in a curl. Muscovys do not, but they are generally accepted as being of different origin.

D. N. A. testing will probably prove many of these old suppositions to be either correct or otherwise, and, interestingly, I read recently that when some testing was carried out on the wild Mallard 80% of those tested were impure.

I believe the assumption that the B. E. I. and the Cayuga were originally of the same parentage is sound, since early photos of the B. E. I. show birds resembling a small sized Cayuga. When I was young the acceptance was that the B. E. I. was the original small wild duck which was then crossed with an Aylesbury type of duck to enlarge it into the Cayuga. A pointer towards their close ancestry is that both of the breeds have a tendency to turn white in plumage as they grow older. Also they both lay eggs which can carry a dusky black colouring to their outer shells. Interestingly, I can find no other breed of wild duck, including the Mallard, which lays eggs with this peculiarity, which would lead me to believe that they were an individual breed in their own right.

An illustration of a quartet of the 'Old variety of Black East Indian ducks' in Cassell's Poultry Book.

131

This point is raised by Stephen Hicks in the books entitled 'Encyclopaedia of Poultry'. When discussing the various breeds of ducks he lists the B. E. I. under the heading of Domestic Ducks rather than in the Wildfowl section. His reasoning is that Darwin referred to the birds under the name of Labrador and then went on to state that Black Ducks bred true and could be classed as a breed. Darwin also quoted their similarity to the Black North American duck, especially in their table qualities. This point is frequently mentioned by many of the old writers. An intriguing piece of the 'jig-saw' is that Black ducks have been referred to by many different names. These include Buenos Ayrean, Black Brazilian, Labrador, Ceylon and Dusk.

In many of the poultry breeds their name has been assumed from either the area in which they were first located e.g. Brahmas from Brahma Pootra, or alternatively the port from which they sailed, as with the Ancona fowls. Presumably, Pekin ducks assumed their name in this manner. Certainly the Aylesbury was called by the area of its origin.

In the book 'The Illustrated Book of Domestic Poultry' written by Martin Doyle in 1854 there is a heading 'Black Labrador Ducks'. The piece goes on to say that the Zoological Society received some of these birds from Buenos Ayres, but a Mr Dixon believes the correct name for them is the Black East Indian, as he believes that they originally came from India, but were shipped via Buenos Ayres. His description of the birds written some 150 years ago is remarkable. It is as follows:- The drake's body is black with a greenish purple shade pervading it, the bill is also black with a tinge of green, the neck, back and larger feathers of the tail and wings are lustrous with mineral green. The duck is described as being of plainer dress but still tinged with the same colouring.

He then continues to describe how, in the early part of the season, the duck lays black eggs and also that with age the birds can moult white. He then draws attention to their superior high wild duck flavour when eaten. He then states that they are at the present time ranked as being domesticated but feels that they are really mid way between wild and tame and are actually in a transitional state between primitive freedom and the habits of domesticated life.

Harrison Weir in his book 'Our Poultry', which was written in the early part of the twentieth century relates an experience when he was at school in 1836. A fellow pupil brought some eggs to show him. They were a sooty black colour and had been laid by some new ducks which his father had just brought from abroad.

In the 'Illustrated Book of Poultry' written by Lewis Wright there is a statement made by a Mr J K Fowler stating that these little black ducks are to be found in the Punjab, but, surprisingly, Lewis Wright does not comment on the statement, which is unusual for him as he seemed to delight in being rather controversial, but on this occasion seemed willing to accept that they were sports from the Mallard. He then continues to praise the birds for their lustrous colouring, their table qualities and their ability to breed very true, a point which I thought he might have queried if they were to be part bred Mallard. He was very insistent that the best ducks were as small as possible and that he had managed to breed some which were below 2 lbs in weight, which is almost the same as the present day birds.

He continues that many of the ducks around at that time were too large for exhibition purposes and were bred really as commercial table birds where their flesh was top class. He also draws attention to the point that the females, especially, go white with age, but, like the other writers, he never mentions breeding birds which show any form of foreign colouring.

Referring back to the Harrison Weir book, an interesting point is that one of his sons lived for a time in Argentina and when questioned by his father about Buenos Ayres ducks, he replied that he had not heard of them in that country. However, when discussing the Cayuga duck he said that there were plenty of middle sized black ducks living wild, which were very capable of domestication and locally they were called the 'Picasso Duck'. These were basically black, but had a white bar on their wings and had red coloured legs and beak. Which is not quite the description of a Cayuga but proves the point that there existed other types of wild black ducks.

I find it hard to believe that these little black ducks have bred so consistently in both type and colouring for 150 years without being a pure breed, especially when it was only around the period 1850 that the selective breeding of birds became normal procedure, and thus the formation of breed clubs developed.

I have studied the colour photographs in several large volumes covering Wildfowl and none of them appears to offer any solution to my theories. The Scaup is quite close in many ways and has a 'dished bill', a point which is a

133

fault in the B. E. I. and when breeding both the Cayuga and the B. E. I. is hard to eradicate, which suggests to me that it was a feature amongst the original black ducks. I have bred both of these breeds over many generations and have never bred one which showed any sign of colouring other than black and certainly no sign of any eye stripe as in the Mallard. It seems incredible that all these beautifully green sheened self black ducks have descended from either an accidental mating amongst the wildfowl or by a freak sport. However, that is what the historians would have us believe. I cannot prove my belief that the B. E. I. was originally a pure wild duck in its own right, but conversely I suppose, neither can the historians prove their case at the present time.

I will, however, close this chapter by relating a short story which was mentioned almost by accident during a recent telephone call. The subject being discussed was only remotely connected with Poultry, but my caller mentioned that he had recently been speaking to a gentleman in southern China, who commented that he had eaten for his evening meal a hairy feathered bird which had black skin and flesh. Apparently these birds live wild around the area and are then caught and used for human consumption.

These fowls have received hardly any mention by the early writers, but Lewis Wright draws attention to them when discussing Silkie and Langshan poultry. Langshan birds are of the normal flat feather structure and originated from Lang Shan Kiang which is north of Shanghai. Langshans have been bred there for centuries, but Lewis Wright thought that there might be a link between them and another bird which had been mentioned by a man called Temminck. He called the bird Gallus Morio or Negro Fowl, and he believed that they originated from southern China. Apparently some of the early imports of Langshans carried traces of dark skin and dusky faces.

The Lewis Wright book was written around 1890 when it was apparently assumed that the Morio fowl was a long time dead and gone, presumably lost for ever. Edward Brown in his book 'Poultry Breeding and Production', which was published some 40 years later, again makes reference to Temminck and his Morio fowls. He believed that many centuries ago these birds had crossed with the Red Jungle Fowl, and the resulting progeny could be the foundation of many modern day breeds. I was delighted by this chance snippet of information during a phone call. It adds encouragement to my hope that one day some person will emerge from some remote part of India or perhaps the old island of Sumatra with a basket full of little black ducks.

Shape

A drake with the correct head and body type.

The head on this B.E.I. is too flat without any rise from the bill. The body is a little short and the neck a bit thick.

A duck with a fair head type but the body is too long in proportion to its head

The birds' fabulous green colour, is the feature which immediately attracts new exhibitors to the breed. However, once you have gained more knowledge you will start to place great importance on a bird's shape. Birds with long slim bodies soon become unacceptable as do the ones which are too strong and coarse and become 'chunky' looking and thus lose the breed's sleek and active appearance.

This coarseness may not be confined to the body but can also extend to the head and neck, especially around the shoulders. In common with many other breeds and species the front, i.e. the crop region, is very instrumental in defining a bird's shape and general outline. In the B.E.I. this should be quite prominent and well rounded, then mould gracefully into the body. The body is not short and rounded as in the Call Duck and is well described as being of medium length. The illusion of length is partly controlled by a bird's depth of body. The depth in this case can be quite considerable before becoming out of balance and looking long backed. However, if it is too deep the bird quickly assumes a 'cobby' appearance. The whole point is that all areas are developed in moderation so that when they are combined together they create a bird which is in balance. The neck contributes greatly to a bird's general appearance and in this breed it should only be of medium length and must not be thick or cumbersome looking. The tail is small and blends into the bird's stern so as to be nearly unnoticed apart from the main tail feathers sticking out backwards and on the drake the distinguishing curly feathers curving upwards. The carriage of a B.E.I. is only slightly elevated from being parallel to the ground. Their wings are carried well up to the tail and fit closely into the body, not trailing low or being loose fitting away from the body.

Legs and feet

This variation in colouring also extends to the legs and feet, which ideally are black, but a tendency towards a dark orange tinge can be tolerated in older stock. The length of leg should be long enough to keep the bird's body well clear of the ground to enhance its balanced appearance. More important is the position of the legs. These should be in the middle of the body. Too far backwards or forwards will spoil the birds balance and carriage. When viewed from the front the legs should be neither 'knock kneed', nor 'bow legged'. In ducks the latter is the more common fault where either or both of the knee joints are weak and thus allow the leg to bend outwards.

The points awarded in the standard for carriage, body, head, bill and neck total 40, with the legs only receiving 5 points.

This Ludlow print depicts Black East Indian and Cayuga ducks. The Black East Indians were owned by Mr G S Sainsbury and won, amongst other prizes, the cup at Bristol in 1872.

Head

In every breed a good head is an essential part of the correct bird structure and the B.E.I. is no exception. The bill should not be as short as that of a Call Duck, neither should it be too long and out of proportion to the skull. The beak should be broad and free from exaggerated side serrations, i.e. 'fish billed', but even more importantly it should not have a hollow in the middle and thus become what is termed 'dish billed'. It should mould into the skull at a position slightly lower than the eye. The skull itself should be quite high, though nowhere near as rounded as in the Call. This high skull means a rise from the base of the beak to the crown of its head. In a breed such as the Indian Runner, the beak top and skull should be in one straight line. A bird which is short of rise to the skull is termed 'flat skulled'. This fault also tends to give the bird a long looking general outline. I believe that in many ways the head shape determines the shape and conformation for the rest of the bird or animal. The head size should be in keeping with the bird's body size, and not look out of proportion. The eyes should be alert looking and dark brown in colour. The colour of a B.E.I. beak has often been open to discussion, perhaps not as to the perfect one, which should be black, but more to the amount of tolerance allowed for bad colouring. This defect is more common in drakes than ducks. The standard says that a green or a yellow bill is a serious fault but a grey tip to it can be regarded as less serious and not a disqualification.

Size.

Size carries 15 points and in all breeds of Bantam ducks size is very influential when selecting the best birds. The same is true in the judging of Bantams and Miniatures in Poultry, and has always created discussion and long debate.

In the early stages of a breed's development or creation into a miniature version of an already perfected large breed, the usual saying is, 'As small as possible', which is a useful guideline in the early stages of development. But once a breed has become established and a recommended weight stated in the standard the situation becomes more serious. Weights are fine in principle, but they do not always illustrate the full extent of a bird's size. A small bodied bird which has had a 'good home', and is possibly overfed and a bit fat may weigh more than a larger framed specimen which is short of flesh and condition, therefore not weighing a true representation of its size.

Consequently the often proposed procedure of weighing all the birds in a class is not really practical, especially in small breeds where only a few ounces could become influential. It would be the equivalent of Professional Boxing, with birds or fighters on the weight border line being starved of food and water prior to the 'weigh in'. This system could then be interpreted as using a bird's excessive size as a disqualification, rather than lose some of the points which are allocated for weight in the standard.

I believe that the best way to approach the subject is by using common sense. All the various parts of a bird's bodily construction should blend together and appear uniform. A bird's head may be either too large or excessively small. Its wings may be extra strong in their bone and feathering thus making it look cumbersome. I would rather read a bird's description as being - 'A good all round specimen but a little on the large size', rather than it be disqualified for being three ounces overweight. There used to be a north country guideline which said that 'A good little 'un should always beat a good big 'un'.

The danger is that if we pursue a course of encouraging birds to be continually bred smaller and smaller, we reach a point where 'freaks' are being shown which, in many cases, are not capable of continued, reliable breeding and reproduction.

Colour and Judging

I have grouped these two subjects together to avoid repeating myself, whilst discussing both topics. When judging B.E.I. much of their correctness to standard can be assessed by studying the bird in its showpen, where, hopefully, it will be standing in a natural position awaiting inspection. This is of course part of the exhibitor's responsibility when preparing his birds for showing. He has to make sure that they are properly 'pen trained' and waiting in anticipation for the judge's inspection. The signal for this is usually a slight movement of the bird with a 'judging stick'.

The bird's shape, carriage, position and length of leg can be carefully studied from outside the pen. Much of the head shape and beak construction can be assessed at the same time. An examination of its colouring is different.

The important conclusion to any judging is not to allow yourself to be influenced by any single part of the standard. Simply allow your brain to work as a computor and assess all the bird's good points, whilst downgrading these against its faults, until you reach a hypothetical percentage marking. It is very simple to over emphasise a particular point at the expense of the bird's other good assets. The only exception to this is when a physical deformity or severe mismarking is discovered, in which case these points can be dealt with under the 'serious faults' and 'disqualification' part of the Breed Standard.

Colour.

Colour is probably the main feature of a B.E.I. and to assess it fully the bird has to be carefully removed from its pen. This procedure is not always required in some of the breeds of Waterfowl, (see the chapter on judging in the earlier part of this book). Assessment of a bird can quickly be achieved from outside the pen with easy comparisons with the other birds in the class, but, when you have a large class to judge with several of them looking fairly equal in merit, the deciding factor could be in what you find when they are examined outside their pen. One of the first places to look is the throat area, especially under the bill, where you can often find a patch of white feathers which are objectionable. In an old drake the odd one or two are not too serious especially as most exhibitors would have removed them during their show preparation.

The whole of the breast area extending right up to under the tail can often be the deciding point in your placements. The more intense the green sheen the better and it is surprising how rich a colour the very best specimens can achieve. This area should also be clear of any white feathers. In really bad cases, the upper part of the breast where it extends under the wings can show traces of reddish brown colouring. If large enough in area this fault is bordering on disqualification. It is certainly high on the list of serious faults.

Once the bird is removed from the pen you can attain a better view to check that the lustrous colour on top of the wings is equal to the colouring on the bird's back. If so, it is a good indicator that when you inspect the underside of the wing this will also be a solid black colour. It will not carry the sheen that the top feathering does, but it is required to be as dark as possible. If there are signs of 'dusky grey', or red spangled feathers it is a fault which suggests that at some period in its past breeding grey (Mallard) Call Duck blood has been introduced. This fault is often found in the very small type of duck which again indicates the use of Call genes.

One good indication as to the strength of colour in a bird is to examine the lower part of the quill in the flight feathers. They should be dark rather than grey/white coloured. This examination is often used in Poultry to test the strength of colouring. It is especially done in the Buff varieties, such as Plymouth Rock, Cochin and Orpington. Whilst you have the bird in your hand it is easy to give the head a closer inspection. A ring of tiny white feathers around the eye is very common in old drakes and is to be reluctantly accepted when they are shown in an adult bird class. It is also advisable to look a little closer at the eye. This should be dark brown. In the British standard there are no individual points allocated for the eye, it is simply included in the total of 15 for the head. In the American standards the eyes are allowed 2 points for shape and 2 points for colour. I have just used the expression American standards. This was not a misprint as over there they have 'The American Bantam Association' standard and also 'The American Poultry Association' standard which in some instances varies slightly. On this point they are identical.

Having inspected all the birds and returned them to their pens, it is wise to let them settle for a short while and then give the ones which you have decided will be in your final selection a last, outside the pen, inspection. The standard allocates 10 points for condition. This is a point which can be interpreted in different ways. It could be used to cover the issue of broken feathers or more probably lack of sheen or 'bloom' as it is sometimes called. This feature really is due to condition, but so is the bird's ability to stand in a pen looking 'fighting fit' and just asking for the red card, and it is this small part of the standard that might be the final influence as to how you place the award cards.

A group of mixed coloured Call ducks at Anne Terrell's

141

Silver Appleyard Miniatures and Silver Bantam Ducks by Chris Ashton

It would appear that at the present time there are many people who are confused with the various types of 'Small Silver Coloured Ducks'. We are therefore attempting to overcome this dilemma. Basically, the birds divide into three separate categories.

Firstly, the Miniature Silver Appleyard, which is bred to the same shape and colour pattern as the large Silver Appleyard. It is smaller in size, being only approximately one third of the weight, 3 lb for males and $2^{1}/_{2}$ -3 lb for females.

Secondly, we have a breed which is smaller in size than the Miniature Appleyard and is based on the original Bantam Ducks which were created by Reginald Appleyard. These birds are slightly different in shape and colouring from the Appleyard and, in some respects, have a similarity to the Abacot Ranger. This breed is now called the 'Silver Bantam Duck'.

Thirdly, there is, amongst the various colours of Call ducks, one which is standardised as a 'Silver'. These birds are bred to be exactly the same shape in both body and head as the other colours of 'Calls'. Full details of their colour patterns are included in the section of this book which is allocated to the breeding and judging of 'Call ducks'.

The source of confusion over the breeds would appear to be that when Reginald Appleyard created his delightful Bantam Duck he did not envisage it being a miniature version of the large Silver duck which he had also created and called after himself. The style and colouring of his new development was to be unique to itself. Consequently, in later years, other breeders have developed a bird which is an exact replica of the large Silver Appleyard, i.e. the Silver Appleyard Miniature.

Chris Ashton has spent many hours researching books and contacting the various breeders who had contact and knowledge of Reginald Appleyard's breeding programme. Therefore in the rest of this chapter Chris will describe her findings in detail and also summarise the standards for each breed. [THE EDITOR, SCRIBBLERS PUBLISHING].

Small Silver Ducks

In the early 1980s there were exhibition classes of the **Silver Appleyard Bantams**; nobody had heard of the **Miniature Appleyard**. Yet ten years later the attractive and docile bantam, the ideal pet and good mother, had all but disappeared from the exhibition pen. The miniature had eclipsed it.

After lengthy wrangling and discussions in the late 1980s, the **Silver Appleyard Bantam** officially became the **Silver Bantam duck**, and the Miniature claimed the famous name of Appleyard. Whether this was the right course of events will probably always be open to dispute and the reader will have to gauge the strength of the argument. On the one hand, Appleyard did originate the Bantam, whilst the Miniature *looks* like his full sized Appleyard. To sort out what has happened one has to begin at the beginning with the full sized Appleyard at Ixworth in Suffolk.

The large Silver Appleyard

A painting of a pair of large Silver Appleyard ducks by Wippell in 1947

Reginald Appleyard was a great waterfowl breeder of both the pre and post war years. His Ixworth leaflet shows the medals he won with his geese at the Dairy Show in the 1930s. He was also renowned for his Indian Runners, Aylesburys, Orpingtons and Rouens and wrote his own book on ducks, published in 1937. Very few people seem to have shown waterfowl seriously during the 1940s when there was a dearth of domestic ducks in Britain but Appleyard managed to continue with his stock.

However, he never explained in print how his own breeds, the *full sized* and *bantam* Silver Appleyard originated. He referred briefly to the large duck only, in his pamphlet from the 1930s, produced whilst he was at Ixworth. The Appleyard was the result of an "effort to breed and make a Beautiful Breed of Duck. Combination of beauty, size, lots of big white eggs, white skin, deep long wide white breasts. Birds have already won at Bethnal Green and the London Dairy Show and the Ducklings killed at 9 weeks 6 ½ lbs cold and plucked."

Appleyard probably produced the large silver duck by cross breeding the breeds within his own stock, but, with no written records, the true account was lost when he died in 1964. The same obscurity was also true of his bantam. Almost all we know of the smaller bird comes from John Hall who, as a schoolboy in the 1950s, regularly visited Ixworth. John relates 'I used to call on him often, I must have been an awful pest.' John never wrote down anything either about the bantam so there grew up an assumption that little Appleyards should look like big Appleyards. Here lies the difficulty; the larger sized birds which have a similar colour to the bantam are not the big Appleyards but another breed, the Streicher or Abacot Ranger.

Reginald Appleyard who judged Indian Runner ducks at the Royal Show in 1931.

To add to the difficulties, the large Appleyards seem to have virtually disappeared in Britain by the 1960s, but a visitor to the continent discovered a breeder in Switzerland with some Appleyard eggs. She gave these to a further breeder in Britain, telling him that they were bantam Appleyards. The eggs hatched quite well—and grew into 6 lb. ducks (live weight). They were certainly not a bantam. They were very colourful birds

144

however, and became quite popular as 'Appleyards' in the 1970s. There was a certain discrepancy between these birds and Reginald Appleyard's that people did notice and comment on. They were not nearly as heavy as the original 9 lb table birds.

It was Tom Bartlett who challenged the assumption that these large coloured ducks being shown in the 1970s were the correct Appleyard. Tom publicised a painting done by Wippell in 1947 showing a pair of full sized Appleyards. This painting had been loaned to Tom by Reginald Appleyard's daughter, Noreen Godwin. This, he said, was what Appleyard had, and what we should have again. Wippell's painting clearly showed the drake to have white cheek markings and a silver throat; consequently these face markings have now been recognised as being the original and the correct ones. Tom then set out to produce a smaller version, one third the size of the silver cheeked drake painted by Wippell - the Miniature Appleyard which was developed in the 1980s.

The Silver Bantam duck

Because Appleyard never referred to this little duck itself, even in his Ixworth catalogue, most of the information we have on it comes from duck breeders whose experience dates back to the nineteen fifties. An article appeared on it in a journal in that decade. This article is waiting to be rediscovered and that may be all that there is available in print. John Hall remembers Appleyard saying that the bantam was produced from a white Call drake which crossed with a small Khaki Campbell duck on the river at Ixworth. This statement is at odds with a newspaper cutting, saved by Mrs Godwin, which claimed that the birds were directly descended from the large Appleyards. However, John Hall remembers that the resulting progeny bred true 'like peas in a pod' [Appleyard's description]. The only variation that John remembers in the late 1950s and '60s was in a wildfowl collection where there were Silver Bantam females with yellow-gold wing bars instead of the original colour. These birds, perhaps showing the Khaki Campbell genetic inheritance of the bronze bar, were unfortunately lost.

The Silver Appleyard Bantam appeared in the Standards for the first time in 1982 where it said that the colouring was similar to the large version. Whilst the large sized drake stands there with his prominent silver cheek markings and throat, the bantam drakes of the eighties (which were not figured) always had a solid beetle green head.

This group of ducklings shows the almost black heads of both males and females, and light body feathers. The juvenile colour is very similar to juvenile silver Call. The males will develop the mulberry bib and green head later; this colour phase in their development is exactly the same as in silver Calls.

The bantam female in the Standards was fairly typical of those shown in the eighties. The body was basically white, streaked with grey and buff. The wing coverts were laced with the same colours, the wings bar a bright blue or even indigo. The head shows a typical brown 'hood'. Both the indigo wing bars and the hood are features of the Abacot Ranger—even called the 'hooded' Ranger. In contrast, the hood is a *fault* of the large Silver Appleyard. The legs and beak of this bantam were darker than those of the majority of birds shown but there always was quite a lot of colour variation in these parts. The darker legs may even have been desirable, to keep more coloured feathers on the body plumage, as in this specimen. As with silver Calls, whose colour markings are very similar to those of the Silver Bantam, colour tends to fade over the years in the duck, and she gets whiter.

After 1987, Miniature Appleyards took off in popularity and the Appleyard classes became a bit of a nightmare for both judges and exhibitors. There was no class for the new miniatures, so people new to ducks put them in the 'bantam' classes when they saw the word 'Appleyard'. Confusion reigned.

The breeders knew one from the other but many people didn't and even the characteristics of the birds began to get mixed up.

Whilst people did not understand the differences in colour and type, quite a lot of mixing went on and basically the old Silver Bantam was spoiled. They became too large and the duck acquired too much colour from crosses with the Miniature . It is now very difficult to get good specimens of the Silver Bantam duck and although there may be three or four in a class at a show, none of them recently has been correct for both size and colour. The miniature has ousted the bantam because it is the more distinctive duck. The bantams always looked a bit like a silver Call with a long beak, whilst the colour detail of the miniatures is attractive and gives exhibitors something to aim for.

Breed description—The Silver Bantam

Weight: The 1982 Standards gave the weight as slightly greater than Calls at 24-28 oz in the males and 20-24 oz. in the females. In practice the birds were about the same size as Black East Indians and so weights of 32 oz (2lbs) and 28 oz. are given in the 1997 Standards. Birds being shown at present, in the late 1990s, are larger than those in the 1984/5 show pens.
Carriage varies with the activity of the bird from horizontal when at rest to a sprightly, upright carriage when alert (as in the photograph of the young duck on page 24 of the colour section).
The head is neat and lacks the full cheeks of the Call duck; the crown is also flatter than that of the Call. Beak length is intermediate (in proportion) between the Call and mallard; it is of average length.
The neck is of average length and held in an upright position.
The body is compact, but nevertheless longer than that of the Call
The legs are set midway along the body.
The drake's plumage is similar to that of the silver Call. The glossy green plumage of the head is terminated by a white collar which completely encircles the neck—a characteristic of white birds crossed with mallard/ brown colour. The broken mulberry bib is also a cross-colour characteristic. The mulberry feathers are each laced with white, and the mulberry extends onto the scapulars and along the upper flank feathers. The belly, flanks and stern are, themselves, white. The back feathers are darker, the white ground colour being stippled with black which intensifies towards the rump. The rump and under-tail are black with the typical green sheen and sex curls of

the drake. Tail feathers are grey edged with white .The primary feathers of the wings have a white ground with black stippling on the outer edge. Secondaries (speculum) are an intense blue often violet-green (perhaps a throwback to the Khaki cross which may intensify the colour).

Bill colour is a clear light olive (yellow green), but the bean is black.

The duck's plumage also mimics that of the silver Call female. The basic body colour is white with a contrasting hood of fawn, especially in young ducks. The crown and back of the neck should show characteristic dark brown graining, this and the fawn hood becoming less distinct over the year as the feathers get older. The upper breast and shoulders should carry brown mottling and streaking; this is not apparent in very young birds (as in the photograph on page 146) but the colour intensifies mid-season. The rump should also be flecked with the same colours, and the tail. This colour should be maintained on the wing coverts which are dark fawn and grey-fawn with cream lacing. The primaries and speculum are the same as the drake's.

The bill colour on the duck tends to be variable, but is not gun-metal. Most birds have a dull yellow bill with variable brown/black markings on the saddle. Again, this is similar to the silver Call.

Both duck and drake have brown eyes and orange legs.

Silver Appleyard bantam ducks. This duck is very dark on the breast, back and rump. Not typical of the birds shown in the 1980's.

Selecting breeding birds

As with Miniature Appleyards (and silver Calls/dark silver Calls) bantams can also breed a dark and a light variant. The duckling illustrated on page 28 of the colour section is the light, correct variant and will produce the silver drake and the pale duck. However, some matings produce dark ducklings. Their fluff shows the camouflage pattern of the mallard, but in a dilute form, very much like dark silver Call ducklings which are instantly recognisable from the standard silvers at this stage.

Although the darker variants were rarely shown, they were quite useful in the breeding pen because they would keep the colour on the silver ducks which otherwise tended to become too light. The ducklings and the adults always produced the light or dark variant; there were no 'in-between' birds. If light birds were always selected they would breed only light birds but the ducks, in particular, became too pale.

When we bred these birds in the 1980s they were very healthy and did not suffer from structural deformities. The ducks liked to lay a clutch of a dozen eggs and go broody but would carry on laying if the eggs were taken away. They were very tame and easy to keep, rarely getting ill or suffering from bad legs.

The making of the Miniature Appleyard

In poultry terminology, the miniature is a scaled down version of the large size bird. That is what Tom aimed for in the Miniature Appleyard. These birds are one third the size and weight of their heavy-weight relative; they are a replica of the full size in markings. As a smaller replica of an existing breed they are the first true miniature in domestic waterfowl. Bantam poultry should be one quarter of the full sized birds, and this more exactly fits the Silver Bantam which only weighs 32 oz (it was similar in size to the Black East Indian) in contrast to the 40-48 oz of the miniature.

Tom's breeding programme of the 1980s to produce the miniaturised bird culminated in the beautifully photographed birds publicised in *Fancy Fowl* in 1986. The duck in particular looks like fine porcelain in the delicate creams and fawn splashes and is a perfect replica of the 7-8 lb. duck photographed beside her.

There were however, problems with the drakes. With random mallard and white crosses, males often develop a broad collar of white which extends up the back of the neck—the 'scarf' problem as Alison Harvey, a keen Miniature Appleyard breeder, once called it. This fault can be seen as a faint pale mark in the same line of ducks too if you really look for it.

Breed description—the Silver Appleyard Miniature

Weight: Miniature Appleyards are 1/3 the size and about 1/3 the weight of the full-sized Appleyards : up to 3 lbs in the drake and $2^1/_2$ lbs in the duck. They are larger than Black East Indians and Silver Bantams.

Carriage: These birds are a replica of the full size, so they should carry themselves in the same way, slightly upright.

The head is fuller and bolder than the Bantam and the neck correspondingly slightly thicker. The bill is also of medium length but slightly broader than that of the Silver Bantam, in proportion and in keeping with it being a replica of the large Appleyard.

The body is broad and well rounded but of moderate length so that it is not so rounded as a Call.

The drake's plumage is marked as in the large Appleyard. The head and neck are black-green but the throat is silver-white or flecked with silver-white; the margins of the pale throat have green feathers interspersed with the white. The silver eyebrow and cheek markings (the male counterpart of the distinctive light markings of the duck's face) are a feature of the breed and must be present, as well as the light throat. A white neck ring completely encircles the neck, dividing the claret feathers from the green and silver head. The claret bib, as with other cross-colour breeds, is to some extent broken on the centre of the chest, though a wide, pale central band is not desirable. The claret feathers are each tipped with a white fringe. Drakes have varying degrees of claret along the upper flanks. Some are clean-bibbed, others have heavy claret splashes along the upper flank. A compromise in the degree of this colour is perhaps needed to maintain the blue speculum. Lower flanks are pale grey (the effect from the typical mallard feathers with stippled pencilling over a white ground). The underbody and stern are white. The back feathers are claret-tipped near to the neck but become white with heavy, dark grey mottling before changing to glossy black-green on the rump and undertail.

The primary wing feathers are grey and white, followed by the secondaries with an iridescent blue speculum outlined with black and white bars. Colour should be maintained on the wing coverts and the scapulars which should

also have an outer coloured edge of chestnut to enhance the colour of the drake. There are variations in the degree of colour on the primaries, coverts and scapulars. If the birds become too light, then the blue speculum is lost; too dark and the claret becomes too solid and the silver effect of the plumage lost. Maintaining the correct colour is a balancing act.
Bill colour should ideally be as the large Appleyard, a yellow-green.

A group of Miniature Silver Appleyards in the snow at Chris and Mike Ashton's (UK)

The duck's plumage is also marked as in the full-sized bird. The overall impression is of a silver, colourful duck. The head, neck, breast and body are silver-white which contrasts with the band of fawn feathers which run down the back of the neck to join the fawn back feathers without a break. This continuous band of fawn and the silver throat are a distinctive feature of this duck. She is also distinguished by her mallard-pattern face markings. As in the wild mallard, a dark line of feathers passes through the eye giving a pale band above and below and, in the birds in these photographs, a lower dark band as well. In Wippell's original painting of the large sized Appleyard, these dark lines were not so pronounced, but the lines do vary according to the strain and the season. They tend to be slightly more defined in the Miniature Appleyard ducks than the large ducks but should not become too heavy.
The breast of the duck should be silver-white and not be closed by fawn feathers. Fawn feathers extend along the flanks and are flecked with brown. The back and tail feathers are similarly coloured.

Primary feathers are white with brown-grey solid colour changing to peppering. The speculum of the secondaries is blue with black and white bars as in the drake. The wing coverts should not be flat white; fawn with white is preferable. The scapulars may be streaked similar to the flank feathers but some strains show a distinct v-shaped pencil in the darker brown mark.

Bill colour is as the large Appleyard—yellow with a brown saddle.

In both sexes, the legs are orange and the eyes hazel.

Selecting breeding birds

Colour

Breeding for colour always presents problems where the breed is derived as a cross from long established colours for there is inherent instability in the phenotype—the outward expression of the genetic makeup of the bird. From the same parents a variety of colour intensities can be bred which is actually quite useful as the experienced breeder can select the best mating for the breeding pen and also the best colour for the show pen. There are 30 points for colour in the Miniature in the forthcoming BWA standards so colour is given a great deal of emphasis in this breed.

As in the large Appleyard, and the silver/dark silver Call, and the Silver Bantam duck, you can get light and dark variants out of the same hatch. The light variant always hatches as yellow duck with a dark stripe (almost black) along the length of its head. In both the large and Miniature Appleyards, Tom Bartlett considers that this yellow duckling with the stripe is the correct bird; it will produce the correct colour in the females rather than a dark brown. It also produces silvery males but there is also a tendency for the white throat of the drake to get too broad a band, and for both sexes to lose their blue speculum. One therefore has to balance this lack of colour occasionally with a darker bred (dilute mallard) strain. The ducklings look quite different from the yellow ones on hatching but when they are adult it is often the darker coloured males which do better in the show pen because they retain more of the claret colour on the breast and scapulars. Nevertheless, if this claret becomes too heavy, then the bird also becomes a darker grey on the flanks and even the underbody (like the dark silver Call drake, for these are similar genes for colour). In this case the drake is too heavily marked and should be penalised.

Because the colour is such a key point, the ducklings should not be sold too early. The drakes will not reveal their face markings until at least 16 weeks old and to wait twenty weeks is better. The worst ones will end up with no face markings in some strains. Also the ducks change their colour intensity as they grow and can fool you. Some of the prettiest birds at ten weeks are too pale and uninteresting by twenty weeks. You have to keep an assortment if you want to do well at the shows with these birds.

As well as varying over the year, colour also varies with age. Good ducks tend to be at their best in their first and second year. In their second year though you may have to wait until the later autumn months for the best colour to be fixed. The yearling feathers can be rather blotchy to start with and need a few months to become streaked and pencilled. These older birds are often the best for a spring show where they can beat the other coloured breeds; they hold their condition well.

Note that just as large Appleyards should not be muddled with Abacots, Miniatures should not be muddled with bantams. The key colour differences of the plumage are the same, i.e. Appleyard ducks have eye stripes and lack the Abacot brown hood. Appleyard males also have silver face markings and a pale throat whereas Abacots and bantams have a solid green head. Just to complicate the issue, it is possible that, in the past, the bantams did have silver face markings. This was prior to the 1980s.

Colour strains

At present, getting the balance right for colour is probably complicated by this being a relatively recently 'fixed' breed, for there are different strains of miniatures. Tom Bartlett manufactured his own, but other breeders probably did too. Ours were bred from a small, beautifully marked local farmyard duck and were nothing to do with Tom's. Tom's produced beautiful females and ours produced perfectly marked males. Reggie (who hatched as a dilute mallard duckling) won his class many times because of his perfect shape and face markings. The ducks were all right and often did quite well but were usually beaten by either Harvey's, Terrell's or Bartlett's.

At a later date we crossed our line with Alison Harvey's attractive duck line which probably led back to Tom Bartlett's. Crossing this 'duck line' with our 'drake line' was disastrous. Not only did the drakes often have solid green heads (a fault of the duck line) but the feathers of the ducks were also spoiled. The beautiful ticks and pencils degenerated into a mossy pattern. As many poultry breeders have found in the past, intricate colour patterns have to be worked at, and a very selective breeding programme followed to achieve the best.

Type

As well as the colour, the 'type' or shape of the breed is still rather variable too because it has been 'made' recently. Some of the worst specimens resemble a rather pale mallard; some indicate the influence of the Call. In the 'mallard' types, not only is the colour too dark but the bird is racy and has a long bill to match. So, as well as choosing birds with the typical Appleyard colour, breeders and judges should also be selecting the typical Appleyard compact shape instead of the racy 'wild duck' .

Vigour

At present, Appleyards are easy to breed. The problem with ours is stopping them because, in a fox-proof pen, they will lay a clutch of a dozen eggs and sit tight. Many people keep them as broodies because they are such good sitters. Also, they should not suffer from deformities. If you get a pair that do breed badly, try a different strain because there is no need for this.

Because they have been 'made' recently, they are very good layers. If you manage to find the eggs and take them away, you can collect eggs from March until June or even July without a very long break over this season. You can get well over one hundred eggs. In fact, if you wanted to breed a small, whole duck for the table, this bird would be ideal. Unlike Calls, they are easy to hatch and to rear and this is reflected in the price of the average bird. A top quality one, though, is no mean achievement and the price should be commensurate with the quality.

The development in the showing of Appleyard and Silver Bantam ducks.

To trace the progress in the exhibiting of both these breeds of duck, we have used, as a guideline, the results from the National Federation of Poultry Clubs who hold their annual show in the Bingley Hall on the Staffordshire Agricultural Society showground. This show has for many years hosted one of the British Waterfowl Association's Championship shows. In the period of the 1970s the classification for all types of small duck were grouped together under the heading of 'Ornamental Waterfowl', which included breeds such as Mandarin, Carolina and Teal etc.

In the year 1980 the emergence of domesticated small ducks was becoming apparent so the N.F.P.C. schedule allocated classes for A.V. Call duck and also one class combining the Black East Indian and the Bantam Appleyard duck or drake, all in the one class which attracted 11 entries.

The 1981 schedule continued with the same classification and this year attracted 12 entries for the B.E.I./Appleyard combined class which included the names of Tom Bartlett, John Hall, Fran Alsagoff and Vernon Jackson.

1982 saw a further development. It was decided to split the class into separate breeds, the reason being that the B.E.I. appeared to be the dominant breed. This was proved to be correct when they attracted 11 entries, whilst the Appleyards could only muster 4. These were exhibited by Tom Bartlett, Fran Alsagoff, John Hall and Roy Pryce.

Special models, sponsored by Tom Bartlett, were produced for the 'Best of Breed' awards at Malvern in 1987. These were sculpted by Cliff and Jenny Heap and the awards were featured on the front cover of Fancy Fowl,

This rather small entry did not deter the show's ambitions to have classes for all breeds of Waterfowl in both Ducks and Drakes, consequently, the 1983 schedule had now got 2 classes for the Bantam Appleyard and interestingly the entry increased to 8 ducks and 6 drakes. New names were added to the list and included A Newland, D Bullen, Mrs Dodson and G Hicks.

By 1984 the interest in all types of small ducks was increasing fast and Stafford attracted 29 birds, whilst the Poultry Club National at Stoneleigh received 20 birds.

A photograph of a bantam duck where the 'hood' has faded. The duck is paler than the ideal but otherwise correct in colour although she is too large.

1984 entries at Stafford Show: National Federation of Poultry clubs.

Bantam Appleyard duck

373 A.M.Newland	380 J&G Bridson
374 B.J.Russell	381 T W Bartlett
375 M Rubery	382 A M Newland
376 A.M. Newland	383 Mrs S. Bealey (first)
377 Mrs S Bealey	384 Mrs C A Dodson
378 A M Newland	385 Mrs F Alsagoff
379 A M Newland	386 Roy Pryce

Bantam Appleyard drake

387 Mrs S Bealey	395 Mrs S Bealey
388 A M Newland	396 A M Newland
389 A M Newland	397 C A Dodgson
390 J&D Bridson	398 J&D Bridson
391 D P Smith	399 T W Bartlett
392 A M Newland	400 Mrs F Alsagoff
393 B J Russell	401 Roy Pryce (first)
394 A M Newland	

Bantams were very popular in the 1980s as you can see from the fairly large classes at Stafford in 1984, and at the Poultry Club National at Stoneleigh, 1985 (below). The birds in the show pen were very consistent, just as Appleyard described them, 'like peas in a pod'. It is to the credit of the judges that at these shows birds belonging to the same owner were placed first on both occasions.

Silver Appleyard Bantam Drake

3793 J Turton
3794 Mrs S Bealey
3795 A M Newland
3796 D P Smith
3797 T Bartlett
3798 J Hall

3799 A R Crisp
3800 Miss P Middleton
3801 Mrs S Bealey (first)
3802 Roy Pryce
3803 A M Newland

Silver Appleyard bantam Duck

3804 A M Newland
3805 Mrs S Bealey
3806 P Middleton
3807 M Rubery
3808 Roy Pryce

3809 Mrs S Bealey (first)
3810 AM Newlamd
3811 John Hall
3812 A R Crisp

The Best of Breed awards at the B.W.A. Championship show which is held at Malvern are recorded as follows. They commence in 1987, but it was not until 1994 that the Silver Bantam received its own separate award.

In 1987, there was only one class labelled Miniature Silver Appleyard, so Miniatures and Bantams were entered in the same class. The judge, Pat Lawrence judged it according to the Silver Bantam standard as the Miniature Appleyard, at that time, was not in the *Poultry Club Standards*. In 1988 and afterwards, Miniatures dominated the class and it was judged according to this new breed's characteristics. In 1994, the classes of *Silver Bantam* and *Miniature Crested* were added. Pat Lawrence donated the Silver Bantam trophy, and the British Waterfowl Association the Miniature Crested trophy.

The growth in popularity of the Miniature Appleyard has held steady in recent years. The entry at the 1997 P.C. National was 12 birds, whilst the Federation show attracted 19 entries. The Silver Bantam attracted 6 exhibits at each of the shows from four different breeders.

Calls and Bantam Ducks at the BWA Champion Waterfowl Exhibition (Malvern)

Date	Call	BEI	Miniature Appleyard	Silver Bantam	Min'ture Crested
1987	T Penny	Peter Kyles	C&M Ashton	—	—
1988	T Penny	John Hall	Tom Bartlett	—	—
1989	G Owen	S Salmon	Tom Bartlett	—	—
1990	—	P Payne	D. Pritchard	—	—
1991	WR Sumner	P Middleton	Peter Kyles	—	—
1992	Millward/Owen	P Payne	A Terrell	—	—
1993	P Meatyard	—	A Terrell	—	—
1994	C Pears	F Fisher	A Terrell	J Gregory	J Benwell
1995	C&M Ashton	J MacQuaker	C&M Ashton	Ivor Parrish	Vernon Jackson
1996	S Philpott	J MacQuaker	C&M Ashton	Alex Barton	Carl Donner
1997	G&S Barnard	J MacQuaker	J Neal	Alex Barton	John Hall
1998	C&M Ashton	J Hoyle	C&M Ashton	M&A Carson	S Bray-Hinchliffe

Miniature Crested by Ian Kay

Crested ducks which are bred in a miniature version are a relatively new creation. They were first developed by Roy Sutcliffe during the late 1980s. Roy lives at Keighly in Yorkshire and is a top class stockman in many different species. He has a philosophy that when you are creating or rejuvenating any breed you use the best birds possible. There have been instances in the past where breeders have mated such a breeding pen and used their second string selection - not Roy, he used the best son from the standard sized Silver Appleyard crested duck which had previously won the B.W.A. Championship Show mated to a Silver Call duck. From this progeny the only drake with a sign of a crest was put back to his sister and representative birds were produced. The first ones to be seen in public were at the Rare Breeds Show and Sale in 1992. They attracted much attention and were eventually sold for over £100 per pair.

The origin of the standard sized crested duck is in many books quoted as being unknown, which is quite surprising for a breed so recently introduced to this country. No mention is made of them in any books written during the nineteenth century. The Bali duck which is described as being indigenous to the island of that name, was first imported to this country during the 1920s by Mrs Chisholm. The birds had quite a large 'pompom' on their head, with a body shape resembling a three quarters upright Indian Runner.

A White Bali duck exhibited in 1925 by Mrs Chisholm. (photo A. Rice)

It would therefore be logical to assume that the Bali was responsible for the original creation of crested duck, possibly in Holland, which had great connections with the Dutch East Indies where Bali is situated.

Harrison Weir was a very respected author and artist who in the early part of the twentieth century published the book 'Our Poultry'. In the section devoted to crested Ducks, he referred to them as the 'Top-Knotted' duck. He believes that the birds are of very ancient origin and are featured in many of the old Dutch paintings, where they are shown in a variation of colours including White, almost Black and Splash.

He continues to state that the birds were at one period very common around the English farmyards. They were considered to be excellent foragers, which were easily reared, and good layers.

Apparently Surrey Zoological Gardens had for many years displayed the birds in a Mallard colouring and their offspring were in great demand when offered to the public. He kept the breed himself and considered his stock to be the best in the country, having very large 'topknots', which were composed of long and full sized feathers moulded into a global head dress. Due to various circumstances he lost his foundation stock and eventually reached the conclusion that the breed had become extinct in Britain at that period of time.

Harrison Wier in 1903 illustrated the Crested Duck with a top-knot, which he owned, and also a head of a duck showing the fatty excrescence at the base of the skull.

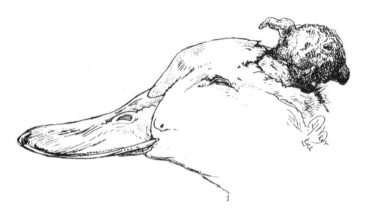

The above drawing by Harrison Weir showing his own stock illustrates the breed exactly as it is at the present time. It seems strange for such a hardy breed to have become extinct, especially as they are capable of crossing with other breeds and still retaining the genes to reproduce crests even after several generations.

The standard of the Crested Duck allows them to be bred in any colour or pattern of colours, preferably in symmetrical markings or pure white. The body is long, broad and moderately deep, with a full and well rounded breast moulding into the body. The neck is of average length and slightly curved. Their carriage is fairly upright at around 35 degrees and their whole appearance is one of an active and alert forager which is capable of laying a good quantity of eggs.

160

The main feature is their head for which a total of 35 points is allocated, 25 of which is for the crest. This should be situated in the centre of their head and be firmly placed. It should be large and globular in shape with the feathering being tight and not open in density, or as it is often called 'loosely feathered'. The bill is long and broad, not dished, and should be set nicely in the head at a forward looking angle, not 'down faced'.

Carriage and body shape are both allocated 15 points, with legs and feet only receiving 5 points. This would appear to be a low mark for a utility breed of duck, which should have a sound pair of legs to enable it to be active.

The breeding of Crested Ducks in either the large or miniature version requires careful selection. In many other breeds where certain features are developed to extremity, lethal genes can be created - Scots Dumpy Fowl with their very short legs are a perfect example,- therefore your breeding pen should be restricted to birds with sufficient crest to breed the correct showing stock without being over the top, In the attempt to breed the perfect crest some stock will have a multiple of crests or tufts of feathers. There will also be ones where the crest falls to one side rather than standing upright. These birds are suitable to use as pets or display birds, but are very limited in their use as breeders.

Another feature of the breed is probably closely linked with the afore mentioned lethal gene. It is that some ducklings can be very short in their body and have either a 'Roach Back' or 'Wry Tail', this deformity can also extend to a 'Twisted Neck'. These birds are only 'culls' and should certainly not be bred from.

When Crested are on public display they always create a great deal of interest. They are a breed to be recommended to newcomers who will find them friendly with the ability to be good egg layers. They can have a long and active life and surplus stock is always in demand.

The situation regarding exact colouring may well be more specifically defined in future years with several colours other than self white having a standardised colour pattern, which could create an added interest to the breed as it has done with the Calls. However, it may be that birds of any colour and with an attractive colour pattern can be bred and shown, proving to be the breed's appealing feature.

Weights:- Drake, 2.5 lbs. Duck, 2 lbs.

Terms Explained

The Teenage stage
This is the stage when the birds are in the process of feathering, and when one looks over the pen one despairs. I do believe the beak reaches its full potential and the rest of the body follows. One has a tendency at some stage to look at the youngsters and despair for they all appear to be hopeless. A miracle occurs given time and suddenly one perceives a bird or two that possibly might be quite good!

Filled up or keel heavy
This is a term used by breeders to indicate that birds are either coming into lay or are laying. The back end of the duck from behind the legs to the tail begins to enlarge and take on a rounded shape.

Downfaced
This indicates that the dome on the head of the bird is deficient, giving the appearance that the bill is facing down with the head sloping up and back from it. It is a bad fault but if the bird has a good body consideration should be given as to whether it is used in the breeding pen and time should be given to the young bird as this condition will improve in some cases.

Boat shaped
This is self explanatory for the duck is narrow in depth and long in body. I suppose the best description would be to say it represents a gondola or native war canoe with a figurehead!

Tipped
This is a condition which I have only experienced in drakes. It can be best described as the legs being placed in the wrong position on the body of the bird, being situated too far back. The bird walks tipped forward and there seems to be more of him in front of the legs than behind. Presumably this condition is hereditary. I have not used a drake showing this condition but a very few do crop up from time to time. Why it should be restricted to the drake I don't know, but to date I have never had a duck like it. Possibly the condition is passed down through the male line.

Slipped wing or Angel wing
This is where the wing turns out and develops at right angles to the body. It is not a condition I am familiar with in my Calls although I have heard of it

being present in Calls. It is my opinion that it is hereditary and that birds developing this condition should be culled. Birds in the wild would not survive, being unable to fly and being vulnerable to the first predator that happened along. It is extremely ugly to look at and not something I would want to see in my breeding pens.

A white female Call with a dropped wing.

Dropped wing
This seems to occur in the smaller birds more so than in the bigger stronger ones. There is a school of thought which says that it is caused by giving too much protein in the early stages of growth, thus causing the blood feathers to fill up with blood too quickly causing the wing to become too heavy before the muscles have developed sufficiently to hold up the weight. Again I an slightly sceptical and feel that there is a case to assume that it is a weakness.

If the bird is of sufficient merit and one is loath to part with it the best course to be taken is to cut the flights once the feathers are fully developed thus taking the weight off the wing. In the following year the bird will moult out these trimmed feathers and hopefully the muscles will have developed sufficiently to hold up the wing. Some people favour pulling out the flight feathers thus taking the weight off the wing for a short period until the feathers are regrown. If the bird in question is small, one is putting it to the unnecessary stress of asking it to grow a whole new set of flight feathers.

Different Types of Travelling Boxes.

In Britain where the average journey to a show or sale is usually fairly short in distance, some type of enclosed basket, cardboard box, or plyboard based box is the common type of container used when transporting small ducks.

In larger countries like America where the journey can be of a long duration, transporting crates are the accepted method of transport. These are usually made of ply board sides and back with wooden doweling used as vertical bars for the front section. These boxes allow the birds plenty of freedom and fresh air with the additional advantage of being able to feed and water them when you stop for a break in your journey. This can easily be accomplished by simply hanging their pots on the box front and the birds soon get used to popping their heads through the bars and helping themselves without messing up the bedding in their box.

Darrel Sheraw is a great believer in this form of transport. The boxes he has designed are mainly for two birds. These are separated by a divider in which a series of holes have been made which enables the birds to communicate with each other without the problem of them getting soiled. He says that ideally these boxes are 10 inches high, which enables the birds to stand up and walk about, but this figure can be reduced to 7 inches and still be adequate, especially for short journeys.

Here in Britain the most common container is a strong cardboard box. There are plenty of them available in this age of 'throw away', especially amongst the arable farmers with their surplus spray can container boxes. These are made of very strong cardboard, and can be used for all classes of small ducks. One important point is that they are strong enough to allow you to cut quite large holes in them, allowing you to hang their food and waterpots as in the American system. Additionally you must be sure to cut plenty of ventilation holes in the box sides and back. It is very easy to underestimate the amount of ventilation required when birds are in a confined space. This point is still relevant even in the winter months, especially when travelling in modern day vehicles, all of which have a built in heating system. I stress this point regarding 'flow of ventilation' as it very easy to accidentally cover up some of the air holes when loading boxes into your vehicle. Another advantage with the cardboard box is that should they become damaged or infected in any way they are easily disposed of.

The old fashioned travelling container was made from a cane and wicker frame, which was lined with either sacking or calico, both of which provided excellent ventilation whilst at the same time excluding direct draught. These baskets were ideal. They are still made, but are rather expensive and do require a certain amount of care if you wish to preserve them in top class order.

The shape of a travelling box should be calculated to suit the breed it is designed to carry. In Waterfowl this is fairly consistent amongst the breeds, with most of them being longer than they are wide as opposed to Poultry, where there is quite a variation in shape, especially in depth of the body. There is also the vast difference in tail length between males and females.

Graham and Sandra Barnard pose beside their ingenious duck travelling boxes, which are made from collapsible plastic boxes which are sold flat packed in D. I. Y. stores. They make their lids and dividers from plywood and the boxes are stored flat to save space.

In size, the box should either be large which then allows the bird to turn in a complete circle without damaging its feathering, or alternatively, the box, or compartment of a box, should be so narrow that it holds the bird in a comfortable but stable position without being able to turn round. The big problem is when the compertment is midway between the two alternatives and allows the bird to just manage a turn, but, in doing so, damage its feathers. Birds carried with close fitting sides are usually very comfortable.

They feel secure and are safe from rolling around when the vehicle manoeuvres around bends etc.
The box floor should be liberally bedded with either sawdust, shavings or wheat straw. A combination of them can be very successful, the straw allows the bird to nestle down in a very natural position, whilst the sawdust absorbs any moisture.

I find that ducks do enjoy travelling as a pair, but, especially with white ones, there is a risk of arriving at a show and finding that one of them has managed to decorate itself with a large green stain, illustrating that it has sat too close to the other one at a very inappropriate moment! The answer to this is to separate them with a 'friendly divider' as in the Darrel Sheraw crates.

One vital point which is overlooked by many exhibitors is the question of 'travel sickness'. Not all birds take readily to a car journey, especially for the first few trips. It is always advisable to plan your journey to arrive in plenty of time before judging. This gives the birds a settling down period, or better still, if it is a Championship show, arrive the night before. All of us have heard the comment from a beaten exhibitor 'My bird doesn't look as good today as it did at home!' This is very often caused by the stress of travelling.

More information on Call and other bantam ducks can be obtained from the following organisations:-

The Poultry Club. Mr Mike Clark, 30 Grosvenor Road, Frampton, Boston. PE20 1DB

The British Call Duck Club. Graham & Sandra Barnard, Ty Cwmdar, Cwrt-Y-Cadno, Llanwrda, Carms. SA19 8YH. 01558 650532

The British Waterfowl Association, Mrs Roz Taylor, Gill Cottage, New Gill, Bishopdale, Leyburn, N. Yorks. DL8 3TQ. 01969 663693

The Domestic Waterfowl Club. Mr M A Hatcher, 2 Limetree Cottages, Brightwalton, Newbury, Berkshire. RG16 0BZ. 01488-638014

Fancy Fowl

The leading publication to encourage the continued preservation of traditional pure bred Poultry and Waterfowl

Features include:-
: 40 page format : Club news & show reports : Breed summaries
: Breeders Profile/Nostalgia page : Readers letters
: 'Fancy Ideas', General interest page : Extra Waterfowl features
: Foreign representatives reports : Juvenile page

Single copies of Fancy Fowl are available at £2.50 including p & p,
or annual subscription of £26.00 (£32.00 overseas).

Fancy Fowl also publish 2 colour posters, @ £3.00 each including p & p:-
Domestic Ducks featuring 19 different breeds.
British Breeds of Poultry, featuring over 40 photographs.

Payment by Cheque, Postal Order, Visa, Access or AMEX.
Fancy Fowl, Scribblers Publishing Ltd., The Watermill, Southwell Road,
Kirklington, Newark, Notts. NG22 8NQ, ENGLAND.
Tel:- 01636 816222, Fax:- 01636 816111.
e-mail:- fancyfowl@innotts.co.uk

167